SHITBAG SOLDIER

SHITBAG SOLDIER

A CREATIVE NONFICTION NOVEL

LUBRINA BURTON

ERUDITE
PRESS

ISBN: 978-1-958414-22-4

Erudite Press

Goshen, Kentucky 40026

Dedicated to Battle Buddies

DISCLAIMER

DISCLAIMER

This book is a work of creative nonfiction. The events are true to the best of the author's memory. Dialog has been recreated, and names of individuals, places, and military units have been changed.

PROLOGUE

PROLOGUE: HIGH-SPEED, LOW-DRAG

Time slows, and space compresses into the singularity of a blackhole. As I cross the event horizon, the point of no return, my brain captures the pictures that only later emerge.

In one photo, gray skies through a soaked windshield and wiper blades—useless in the downpour—come into focus. Then there's an image of the wet pavement of the *Autobahn*'s slow lane whirling by my passenger side window. A sign for the town of Erdbeeren develops like a Polaroid, followed next by a blurry pic of the blue *Ausfahrt* exit sign to the right of center in the frame. Flashbulbs blow and my mind's film captures a snapshot of the car's speedometer, reading just over 140 kilometers per hour.

What my eyes fail to see, my body races to record and fill in the blanks. There is a hard pull in the opposite direction as I gun the car to the right in order to make my exit. I feel my left foot on the clutch as I let off the gas, my right hand downshifting, my right foot on the brake, the car skidding and almost floating and my frantic turning of the wheel. I'm pushed and pulled as the car cuts a hard left, off-road, through the grass between the *Autobahn* and the Exit ramp. My foot hits the brakes, but nothing. I clamp my eyes shut and pull my body in on itself.

My eyes open wide. I sit helplessly in the driver's seat. I plow down white reflector posts staked into the soft ground. One by one, in a nice rhythmic order—clunk, clunk, clunk—they fall under my car, but do nothing to slow me down. My car is high-speed, low-drag, as we say in the Army. I barrel straight ahead toward the giant *Ausfahrt* sign looming ahead. I pump the brakes again, but nothing. I grab onto the steering wheel as it races toward my face. It is inches away and I tell myself, "I can do this. I can survive."

My mind goes black. It comes back online a few moments later. My back is plastered to my seat, and my car has come to an abrupt halt. Outside my windshield, smoke billows from the radiator, and the sign dangles over my hood. Except for a hissing sound coming from somewhere outside, I hear nothing except the beating of my heart. Or maybe it is the sound of a migraine forming because it is as if my brain is breaking through my skull. There's something tight squeezing my chest wall. Under its compression, I panic. Through my favorite jacket, a black pleather blazer, the most stylish and protective against Germany's cool, wet climate a lower-enlisted soldier can afford, I pat myself down and feel a narrow ribbon of nylon crisscrossing my breast.

"Oh, my God." I hear the trembling in my voice. "My seat belt."

Only then do I realize it is an accident, but somewhere from the depths of my subconscious, I wonder if the Freudian cliché that there are no accidents is true. I fumble with the seat belt mechanism, but I can't get it to release.

For a moment I sit and run my hands along the circumference of the buttery soft leather sport steering wheel, one of the things that drew me to this silver 3-series when I first arrived in Germany just over a year ago. As a twenty-year-old woman-child, I didn't know, or even care, that the fifteen-year-old seat belts on the old '85 Beamer would prove to be its most important feature.

At the center of the wheel, the clean, crisp blue and white circular logo stares back at me like some unblinking eye. I want to apologize to the car for sacrificing itself to save me. I don't deserve to be saved—I don't even know if I want to be saved.

"My car." I scrunch up my face. I want to cry, but I am an American soldier, and I have learned to express all matters of emotion as anger. "My fucking car. Fuck, fuck, fuck." I bang my fists against the steering wheel.

When my hands stop shaking enough for me to free myself from the seat belt, I get out to survey the damage. From the front, I see the post has squeezed the bumper into a V-shape and wedged itself into the hood, just in front of the engine block. The headlights are hugging the pole and almost kiss one another. With the bent and twisted sign planted deep into the BMW and the odd-looking word of *Ausfahrt*, meaning Exit, dangling over me, it strikes me it must be the universe's weird attempt at German modern art, some statement on the affairs of things. I stare in stunned silence as smoke and oil pour out of the car, trying to make meaning out of it all.

Within minutes, two cars pull up behind me. German passersby rush out of their sedans. An older, motherly lady, runs toward me, wailing, "Oh, mein Gott, Oh, mein Gott. Bist du okay?" She throws her arms around me and pulls me back from the car, as if she needs to comfort and protect me.

I stumble backwards, taking in more of the damage. It looks worse the longer I look at it. In a sad German monotone, I reply, "Ich bin okay. Aber mein Auto... Es ist kaputt."

She recognizes my accent or my bad German or both. "Oh, you're American," she says in unpracticed English.

I nod and repeat in English, "My car..."

She rubs my arm. "That does not matter. You are okay."

I put my head to my clammy forehead. "Nein. Das ist egal." Then, under my breath, I mumble the translation, "I don't care."

She clicks her tongue and turns away.

A young yuppie guy in glasses and expensive-looking slacks and blazer jumps out of the driver's side of his new model Audi. He says something to me in German, but the words buzz over my head, and I stare at my mangled car.

"Amerikanerin," the German motherly figure says to the young man whose face flashes his understanding. "Soldatin," she smiles. She must have noticed my Army-issued license plates.

With no regard to his pressed trousers or shined Oxfords, he bends down on his hands and knees in the muck near the front of my car. He places a round piece of plastic, what looks like an old hubcap, underneath my car to catch the oil and fluids spewing onto the ground. In polished English, he tells me we have to keep my car from leaking fluids onto the ground. "The Polizei," he slips back into German. "I mean, the police. They will give you a ticket for environmental damage."

It looks like a warzone on the side of the road. From where my car sits in its muddy grave all the way back a thousand feet to the off-ramp, the tires have dug two deep trenches. I trace the trajectory of the fiery missile from the *Autobahn*, its launch site, all the way to the point of impact. Something smells hot, like burnt rubber mixed with sizzling oil. I swallow the noxious fumes until they come back up in a gagging cough.

A third vehicle parks on the shoulder of the off-ramp. It's a company van and a young man, slim, short, with brown hair, gets out wearing the blue coveralls of the German worker. It's not until the guy is right upon me do I realize that it's my boyfriend Markus. In the nearly ten months we have been together, I think I have only seen him in his civvies.

"Are you okay?" Markus asks in German. "Your face... You're

white as a ghost." Before I can stop myself, my arms are around his neck. I can hardly believe the coincidence of seeing him at this place at this very moment.

Slipping out of my embrace, he puts some distance between us. His German stoicism kicks in. He looks around to see if anyone saw and his cheeks redden with embarrassment. I drop my arms and look down, a hot flush of emotion warming my own face. Off-duty and not in uniform, and caught up in emotion, I have forgotten my military bearing. Still, I feel the burning of a white-hot hatred toward him for his coldness.

"Yes," I say in my native tongue, despite Markus's limited command of English. "I'm fine." Maybe the language and cultural divide or the stress of Army life has finally caught up with us, but I have lost my patience for diplomatic compromise. "But I, my... They're going to, they will..." I am unable to find the words in English or German to explain how I survived the crash, only to be killed at the hands of the United States Army.

I look back at the scene, then over his shoulder at the van parked in the distance. "What are you doing here, anyway?" I shift my focus to Markus. He cocks his head like a puppy who doesn't understand, so I ask again, harsher, in German. He tells me his boss sent him from Bimbleberg on a job to repair an HVAC system here in Erdbeeren. He asks me what I was doing, where I was going.

"I don't know," I say. Then I tell him the only thing I know that makes sense. "I get off work early on Thursdays. I was just driving. I just needed to get away. From the Army, from everything."

Glancing at his watch, he tells me he's late for work. He turns toward the van but stops and shakes his head. "You shouldn't be driving on the *Autobahn* in the rain. It's dangerous."

I narrow my eyes at him.

He doesn't understand danger. He has slept in the same childhood bedroom for eighteen years. He doesn't know what it's like to search for a new life, to leave for the Army at seventeen or travel across the Atlantic at twenty with little more than a duffel bag. He doesn't understand that death stalks me down cobblestone streets and hides behind every tree, every corner. He can't understand why after escaping with my life, I still go looking for death. Perhaps it is my only escape from this world in which I've found myself trapped. It's a world I can't make him understand, where my reality, my truth, even my own self-image doesn't match up with that of the Army's.

I am a soldier. *Ich bin Soldatin.*

I am an American. *Ich bin Amerikanerin.*

How do I tell him what the Army says I am?

How do I translate Shitbag?

CHAPTER 1

THE ME I WAS TOMORROW

Sweat trickles down my spine, giving me an itch in a place I am forbidden to scratch even if I could reach it. My sixty-five-pound rucksack is plastered to my back. My Battle Dress Uniform is sealed to me like a layer of camouflage epidermis. The only trees, like shimmery mirages on the horizon, keep shade forever out of reach. Underneath my combat boots, a sandy dust coats the angry, cracked ground. The dirt road stretches out into the unknown future. The landscape contorts itself around me. In my periphery, I am certain I spy a melting clock dangling from a distant branch.

"It's hotter than the fiery pits of hell." The words escape my head and orbit inside my Kevlar brain bucket. The July sun brightens as I utter my grievances, as if I have offended Helios himself. "I've done cooked out here."

Fort Leonard Wood is about as far from the exotic locales featured in recruiting commercials as you can get. I did not expect my eight weeks of Basic Training to be conducted in paradise, but sometimes I wonder if the Army picked this spot in the Middle of Nowhere, Missouri just to torture young recruits. This is the first time in my seventeen years I have much memory of living outside the hollers and hills of Southeastern Kentucky.

Around the time of the *Star Wars* movie in which Darth Vader meets his end, years before I started kindergarten, but just after my brother stopped using diapers, Mom packed up our lives in Cincinnati. She left my father, who possessed fewer redeeming qualities than Luke and Leia's dad. We moved back to her old Kentucky home. We moved to the side of a mountain, on the banks of a creek where rains routinely made Noah's flood seem like a little high water. We moved up a holler called Stinking Creek, fifteen minutes from a town with no movie theaters, where time forgot. I thought Mom could not have picked a more isolated place with a worse climate. Until now.

At Fort Leonard Wood, the rains come once a week, on schedule, when late Saturday night blurs into early Sunday morning. The heavens burst open all at once, releasing their pent-up emotions, wailing, screaming, and bawling. The wind and rain thrash the exterior walls of the barracks. Thunder claps and trees moan in agony. Outside my second-floor window, beyond the foot of my top bunk, streaks of lightning dart across the sky. A crackling charge crawls across green wool blankets stamped with the words "U.S. Army".

During those first stormy nights, I was certain soldiers on fire guard would burst into our rooms and herd us off to safety in some fall-out shelter the Army had for this sort of thing. By the third week or so, I knew no one would come for us. With my eyes wide open, I lay awake, unable to sleep, staring in awe out my window. "We're not in Kentucky anymore, Toto." I rubbed my tube socks across the staticky sheets. "We're in the Army, now."

In the Army we march on Saturdays. For how long exactly, I never know. We go until we stop. Drill sergeants march us out of the admin area at sunrise, out into the desolate hellscape, then we return as the sun goes down. A paper posted in the barrack's hallway specifies the distance of each week's march. Every week they get longer, more difficult. As we near the end of eight weeks of training, today's march is a grueling test of endurance. From my physics class conversions, I recall one kilometer equals .6 miles. That calculation is from the civilian world, however. I am certain there must be such a thing as an Army kilometer that defies all laws of man and science.

Before the sun has burned off the morning fog, we sling our rucks onto our backs and pick up our M-16s. We march in a standard four-rank formation through the streets until we reach the outskirts of base, where the asphalt breaks off into a brown dirt road. We form two ranks, troops on each shoulder where the grass and weeds grow knee high.

"Here we go," Drill Sergeant Taylor calls out. "Hope y'all bloused your boots. Got to watch out for them private-eating scorpions."

Missouri cannot possibly have scorpions. The drill sergeant must be fucking with us, I am sure of it. I crossed over the Mississippi, not into a different world. It cannot be that far from the fields and hillsides I spent my childhood traversing, where I knew how to avoid the snakes, ticks, and chiggers. Here, however, are stifling temperatures and raging storms unmatched by anything back home. Perhaps in this violent climate where the Army operates, there are all sorts of animals hiding in the weeds I have yet to encounter.

My comrades and I still hold out hope for a better day today than the one before it, although I can smell yesterday's heat wafting up from the ground. We say out loud that today won't be so bad, the gods will bless us. It will be partly cloudy, with low humidity, temperatures in the low eighties, and zero percent chance of precipitation. We will not suffer under oppressive heat or slosh around in water-logged boots. Everything will work out great for us. By this point in our training, though, we are good enough fortune tellers, or at least meteorologists, to know these are stories we tell ourselves.

Drill Sergeant Taylor skips down the middle of formation. Wedged high above the small of his back and between his shoulder blades is his rucksack. His muscles threaten to consume it whole, like a rattlesnake devouring a mouse. He turns his head to look over his shoulder. He crinkles his nose, nods his head, and shoots us a tight-lipped grin favored by all drill sergeants.

"It's a lovely day for a walk through beautiful Fort Leonard Wood, Missouri. Hooah, Privates?"

"Hooah, Drill Sergeant," my fellow recruits and I sound off.

"You don't sound motivated," he says. "Sound off."

"Hooah," we repeat, louder. "We're motivated, dedicated, Drill Sergeant."

"That's more like it." Appeased, he turns around to lead us into the abyss.

By noon, there isn't a cloud in the sky. The sun and temperature are at their highest and morale is at its lowest. A male voice behind me grumbles, "No wonder they call this shithole Fort Lost in the Woods, Misery."

He is right, I think. I wonder if I have died and gone to literal hell. Despite Army-issued SPF 30, the exposed skin of my face, neck, and hands alternates between suntanned and sunburned. At the end of a march, when I take off my boots, the skin of my feet peels off in a single white sheet like a snake shedding its outer layer. My chest crackles from a combination of Midwestern dust particles settling in my lungs and an unshakable barracks cough. My calves seize up at night, my empty stomach aches in the morning, my back spasms all day, and I never know which part of my body will be the next to revolt or when.

As we march into the afternoon, my ruck grows heavier. I look like a hunchbacked G.I. Quasimodo. Under the weight of my pack, I slouch forward until my M-16 dangles in my hands just above my kneecaps. The ruck's straps dig through muscle into bone until I can no longer bear the pain. With the assistance of gravity and without the use of my hands, I give the pack a good heave. I fold myself in two and my ruck does a delicate balancing act in the middle of my back. When that position becomes intolerable, I stand upright again, and the pack slides down until my shoulders catch it by the straps.

Despite the blazing heat, we have stopped only twice since scarfing down part of an MRE at lunch—once to fight off an imagined attack by Commies and again to change our sweaty socks to avoid contracting some foot-eating fungus. I consider asking Drill Sergeant Taylor if we might have a few seconds to readjust our gear or pause for a sip from our canteens. I already see the dirty looks from my fellow recruits, the anger from our sergeant directed at the soldier who admits to being human, woman, weak, so I keep my mouth shut. "Suck it up and drive on," is the Army's official, unofficial motto.

"Just a little farther, privates," my drill sergeant says, like he can hear my thoughts, "and we'll stop up ahead." He promises we will refill our canteens at the water buffalo pulled behind the deuce and a half cargo truck. I fantasize about running up to that little water tank on the trailer, falling to my knees, and suckling at the spigot while cool, fresh water gushes over my head and face into my mouth.

My tongue is as cracked and parched as this Missouri ground. I would sell my soul for a drop of water, but every time I attempt to pull one of my two canteens out from under my rucksack, I discover it just beyond my reach. My LBE ammo belt, like all my other gear, drapes off my ninety-nine-pound frame and barely functions as intended. The belt hangs from the shoulders by a set of suspenders. It snaps shut with a giant plastic buckle that covers up most of my abdomen. Two ammo pouches flank the buckle and sit below where the suspenders attach. On most of the male recruits, the two canteens sit over both hips. On me, the canteens are shoved together in the small of my back.

If I could hold my M-16 one-handed and twist around to remove a canteen from behind my back, and take a sip, all while marching, I could join the Ringling Brothers. I wish I had run away with the circus instead of running off to the Army.

"I bet all y'all privates are wishing you hadn't joined the Army." Drill Sergeant Taylor is definitely a mind reader. "Y'all probably wishing you were sitting on your asses back on your momma's couches right about now."

As if the luxury of sitting around all summer between junior and senior year was one I could afford. I had to find a way out of my small town and a way into college. Perhaps smarter, richer, better-looking kids than I had the privilege of lounging around on their folks' furniture. Maybe their families would allow them to be kids for another year, maybe two after eighteen or graduating high school while they figured things out, but I had already run out of time.

"It's time," Mom said to me back in March, "you learn about being an adult." In the bed of her beat-up Chevy S-10, I stopped shoveling mulch onto her rose bushes that were more thorns than blooms. "You have had seventeen years to be a child," she said, avoiding my eyes and wiping her chestnut hair from her sweaty brow, "more than me or your aunt or mamaw ever had. If you think you can wait until you're eighteen and finished with school to start your life, you have another thing coming. I have taken care of you and your brother by myself all these years, but my time of sacrificing for children is over. You need to have your life figured out before you walk across that graduation stage next year at eighteen because you are not coming back to my house."

Here in my new arid world, I open and close my mouth, like a catfish pulled onto the muddy creek bank, searching for water in the atmosphere. "Just go ahead and tap out right now," the drill sergeant says. "Just fall out to the side if this march is too hard for you. Maybe you don't want the Army bad enough. If that's the case, we don't want you either."

The ground gives way like sand shifting under my feet. I close my eyes and wait for a current to sweep me away, for my body to go horizontal. When the heat of the ground radiates through the soles of my boots, I open my eyes. Waves of nausea wash over me. My shoulders shake, my teeth chatter, and goosebumps pimple my arms. The day's warmth disappears while the sunlight brightens, reflecting off the mica and scorching my retinas.

"Are you okay?" a disembodied baritone voice calls out. "Do you want me to get the drill sergeant?"

Some noise, like a gurgle escapes my throat. I look over my shoulder. Behind me, nothing remains but the blurry outlines of a forgotten wasteland. I pray for the strength to keep moving forward, to escape that which is behind me. I turn and put one boot in front of another. Time evaporates, my consciousness drifts into space, and my body becomes battery-operated. My mind is a black hole of nothingness. The occasional nerve signal reaches my brain stem to let me know I am still breathing, twitching, marching.

I slam into the back of the soldier in front of me. I look around. The formation is stopped. Dirt road and pavement meet, and the orange sun sinks behind the tree line. Soldiers drop their rucks, adjust their gear, and baptize themselves with their canteens.

"Where are we? What time is it?" Ink blots fill my vision when I peer at my watch.

"That's pretty much it for the march," the recruit says. "We made it back to the admin area. Just eleven days and a wake-up, then that's it for Basic. The end."

"If this is the end, why does this feel like just the beginning?"

The shadows lengthen across the dusty ground and an evening wind takes my breath. An ache forms deep in the marrow of my bones. I long to turn the calendars back to yesterday, to return to a genesis that never existed except as a story in my mind. I yearn to go back to that place before tomorrow and be who I might have been. In some other place, some other time, there is a me, a girl. She can figure out who she wants to be someday, even hang on to her own first name. But that's not me. I am not her. I am Burton. I am a soldier.

I check my watch. I down my canteen. I watch the sun go down.

CHAPTER 2

BLOOD FOR INK

On the second floor of a strip mall, I attend classes offered by the same university from which Mom earned her nursing degree when I was still a girl. Downstairs is the Fashion Bug clothing store and the Armed Forces Recruiting Center where I enlisted in the Army Reserves in April 1997, over two and a half years ago. Here at the satellite location, the school offers core classes to kids like me who can't or won't travel from the hills to campus an hour or two up the interstate.

Every Monday and Wednesday evening, my English 102 course meets in one of the classrooms originally designed as office space for the shops downstairs. I sit in the same desk, always sideways, my feet jutting out into the aisle. When he hands out papers, Professor Harris must step over my legs. He never comments. After all, what can he say? I'm in the Army and I've earned the right to sit how I damn well please.

We read books like *The Things They Carried* by Tim O'Brien and write papers on Vietnam. Although officially called Research, Writing, and Rhetoric, the class is more like a special topics course on the war in Vietnam. The outline of my paper about PTSD in

Vietnam Veterans is due next week, the final draft a few weeks after that. I'm so far behind I need two months into next year to catch up. I even forgot my looming birthday in early November until my friend reminded me I was living out the last days of my teenage years. In my defense, a part of me was busy bracing myself for Y2K and the world's end, while the rest of me has been planning my future if we all survive.

Today I am not late. I am fifteen minutes early for class. Outside the room, I pace, wearing bare the low-pile office carpet of the hallway. I've waited until the absolute last minute, but today is the day. I have to explain my situation to Professor Harris, a man with ram-rod straight posture and a lean runner's body. After twenty-plus years, he still holds himself like a young Army officer. Only his accounts of his time in Vietnam and the lines around his eyes give away his true age. While he has always been cordial, his former rank in the military—a lieutenant—as well as his current title, Doctor of Philosophy, makes me feel as if I should salute him before approaching his lectern.

I unfold the piece of paper I hold in my left hand. Reading it gives me courage. It reminds me why I have to do what I'm about to do in a couple of months. Folding the paper back into my palm, then tightening the straps on my dark green Jansport collegiate backpack, I march through the door.

The room does not resemble the one I am accustomed to seeing. Instead of facing the "front" of the room as usual, many of the desks face the whiteboard on the "back" wall adjacent to the door. My professor does not stand in his usual spot at the far end of the room, as I expect. Instead, he is lifting a student desk to face the "front" wall.

Without looking up, he acknowledges my presence. "Hey, there," he says.

"Uh, hello," I say, wondering how he does that.

After turning around the desk, he walks toward the lectern in the back of the room. Gripping it on either side, he lifts with his knees. He lets out a quiet groan, then silences himself.

"Do you need some help with that?" Through my thick auburn shag, I scratch my head.

"I've got it. I just don't understand it, though," he says. "I don't understand why the other professors insist on turning this room around. Every day before class, I come in here and put the room back together the way I need it."

He walks the podium to the new "front". I don't dare point out the obvious that the board is behind us, on what only he calls the back wall.

Then, addressing the unspoken, he says, "I know the board is on the other wall, but that's also where the door is. I cannot be in a position with my back against a window or door. I have explained this to the other professors who use this room. They know my story."

Everyone, including the entire class, knew his story. He told us how as a young lieutenant in the Army he had been in the boonies of Vietnam. Ever since, he said, he needed to see every entrance and exit.

As much as I try to understand his story, I cannot fully comprehend it. I have a feeling that for every word he says, he leaves at least twice as many unsaid.

Professor Harris shoots me a polite smile as he places the podium in its proper location. I walk to my usual desk and throw my backpack into the seat.

I clear my throat. "Dr. Harris," I say.

"Hmm?"

"Uh, I will not be able to make the next class. I know our outlines are due then, but..." Again, I unfold my note. I walk to where he stands behind the lectern. "I was hoping I could turn it in during our next class. I have an excuse."

"You know, I require students to turn in all assignments before the deadline, not after."

I hand him the note. He studies the paper, and a line forms between his eyebrows.

"I know, I said, but I've been busy wrapping up stuff before I ship out. This note's from my recruiter." I grin, certain he will understand now why I should be given an exemption. "He is taking me for my Army physical, down to Knoxville at the MEPS. I mean, the Military Entrance Processing Sta–"

"I know what MEPS is," he interrupts, still staring at the note. My face burns. Of course, he knows. "My question is, what the hell are you doing? Why are you going to the Army?"

I stammer out a few uhs and ums, then I say, "I am already in the Army Reserves. I am just going Active Duty." I thought he knew I was a Reserve soldier. I thought the Army was our unspoken connection. Maybe not.

He drops the paper like it is contaminated.

"But this is Active Duty. This means you're dropping out of college."

"Yeah," I shrug.

"What is the Army promising you?" His cool gray eyes burrow into me.

In the space of a few seconds, every argument, every conversation, every event of the past year leading up to my decision flashes through my brain. It is like reading a chapter from a book. Defying physics and logic, simultaneously, yet subsequently in random chronological order, the scenes from the page manifest on my visual cortex. As I try to formulate a coherent and eloquent response, I turn the pages, following the disjointed story of my life.

The chapter opens with a scene from this past summer in Ft. McClellan. My Quartermaster Reserve unit is training for our new, secondary MOS as Eighty-Eight Mike, Motor Vehicle Operators. I step down from the cab of an Army Five-Ton cargo truck into a hot Alabama July day. My boots and BDUs are caked in red mud, and my comrades greet me with a round of high-fives. I am one of only two drivers who didn't get their vehicle stuck on the one-lane bridge wedged between two steep hills. I feel like some sort of rock star, a conquering hero. Already, I know this will be one of the best times of my life.

That scene unfolds into another. The raging fireball of an Alabama sun is reduced to a white dwarf shrinking behind dark pines. I'm dressed in my favorite green plaid skort and Adidas shelltoes. Under a pavilion, my comrades sit at picnic tables talking, listening to the uncensored versions of songs like "My Neck, My Back" on someone's boombox, and swigging Coronas and Miller Light. I am only nineteen, but the men and women who are my comrades say if a girl drives a truck the way I do, she deserves a drink. They hand me a beer, but I reach for the whiskey. I tell them I've been drinking shit like this from the bootleggers since I was fifteen.

My new battle buddies cheer and say I'm a soldier, all right. They tell me to go after my sergeant stripes as soon as I get back home. Others tell me to forget home, forget the Reserves, and go Active. They tell me stories of being in Germany, when they had more money than bills, racing BMWs a hundred miles an hour down the *Autobahn*, guzzling Jägermeister and beer with buddies, and the hearts of local sweethearts they broke when they left them behind.

A man, a sergeant in his late-twenties resembling a beefed-up Russell Crowe, asks me to go for a walk. Some of the girls and I saw him step out of the shower with nothing but a towel around his waist. He is too beautiful for me, skinny, flat-chested, and knock-kneed. But we are pals. So I confide that I am confused about what to do with my life. I would love to go overseas with the

Army, but I'm in school back home. He asks if I want to stay in Kentucky because of some boyfriend. I laugh and say college guys don't go for me. He says they are just boys, that I need a real man who can handle a real woman. Go, he says, and live before I get tied down. Then he kisses me long, deep, and slow, like I've never been kissed before. Mom would say I don't have enough sense to know he is using me for what's between my legs, but I don't care. Under the stars that pepper the dusky sky, I melt into his arms.

The next scene is out of chronological order. It must have been sometime in early spring, or even late winter, before I went to Alabama. I am in the recruiter's office, downstairs from my current English class, with my brother Jonas as he talks about enlisting. My brother is young, still just a senior in high school, so I have come with him at Mom's request. She thinks because I am nineteen and already in the Army Reserves, that I will protect him, and keep him from making the "wrong" decision. But he was dead set on going into the Infantry, and I couldn't stop him.

I know Mom will say if my brother gets himself killed in the Army, it will be because of me. I'll tell her to blame Jonas's recruiter, Sergeant Meachum, a former infantryman less concerned with pressing his BDUs and cutting his hair than with telling war stories to impress naïve high school boys. Mom ordered me to talk Jonas into logistics or other support, but Sergeant Meachum tells me to convince him to go into the Infantry. I must decide if my alliances are with the Army or my family. Trying to stay neutral, I say Jonas is eighteen. He should do what he wants despite what others say. Seize life by the balls. Go before this town drowns him.

With my brother dangling from his line, Sergeant Meachum turns to snare me next. "What about you?" he asks. "I can tell you want to get out of this place. What's keeping you from seizing life by the cajónes?"

I can see myself in the recruiter's office, slouching in my seat, as I let out a sigh resembling more of a gurgle. Responsibility, loyalty to Mom, even fear of really living, sucks me under, replacing the air in my lungs. But all I say is, "I have to graduate college."

"No you don't," he says. "College, your family, everything will still be here when you get back. If you could go anywhere in the world, where would you go? Hawaii, Alaska, Korea?"

Certain I can lay a trap for him, I say, "You get me England or France and I'll sign the papers right now."

"I can get you Europe," he smiles. "It will most likely be Germany where the Army has the most bases. But I was over there and I can tell you some stories about Germany."

"I bet." I laugh. "But I've also heard when you go Active from the Reserves you start over as a buck Private. I'm not about to give up my E-4 Specialist rank to start over at the bottom as an E-fucking-1."

"I will make sure your contract says you keep your Specialist rank." Again, he grinned. "So, you ready to say fuck school, fuck this town, fuck everything and finally do it?"

Later in the same chapter, it is August in the deep south. Mom and I are on I-75, somewhere in Georgia or Tennessee. The sun creates a watery look on the road up ahead. The AC in her Pontiac Grand Am is no match for a hot environment. Two years ago this July, she and my brother drove out to Ft. Leonard Wood to pick me up after Basic. Her hunk of junk car kept overheating, causing us to stop every few miles. This time, returning home after my brother's Basic Training graduation in Ft. Benning, Mom drives fast, like she's desperate to reach something. Maybe she is trying to outrun the inevitable.

Ft. Benning, I knew was where I belonged, marching in formation with soldiers wearing camo uniforms, shopping in the PX, and even living in the squat, brick Army barracks. I was nostalgic for my days as a Private at Ft. Leonard Wood and Ft. Lee. My brother was now a Private, proud of finishing Basic and giddy about his future. Everything now awaited him, and anything was possible. Never had I seen him grin with his entire face. His eyes were a bright clear blue as he spoke in a new, deeper voice about his assignment to Ft. Campbell, where he would jump out of helicopters and visit home on weekends.

Thinking of my own future conjures up images of dead, wilted flowers. From the moment I signed my Reserves contract, my life has been written. As a seventeen-year-old high school junior, I was both too young and too scared to enlist on Active Duty. Mom was happy to sign for me to join the Reserves. After Basic, the Army legally required me to finish my senior year of high school. My contract mandated that after graduating that following year in 1998, I complete Advanced Individual Training in Ft. Lee for my MOS of Ninety-Two Alpha, Automated Logistical Specialist. After AIT I was assigned to drill once a month and two weeks a year with my Reserve unit in Lexington, until I fulfilled my eight-year obligation in 2005. I enlisted for freedom, for independence, for opportunity. So according to my life plan, I enrolled in an affordable state university near my hometown, a glorified swamp in the Appalachians.

As a little kid I was certain I evolved from a primordial ooze. At the very least I was sure I was adopted, but Mom said that was crazy. She would have never adopted me. She fills up the entire driver's side of the Pontiac. With her large presence, near-constant scowl, and booming voice she is my exact opposite. She likes to show me "who is in charge" by looming over my five-four, hundred-and-five pound frame with her five-foot-six and two-hundred pound body. Strapped into her seat, she cannot intimidate me today.

"As soon as we get back to Kentucky, I'm calling Sergeant Meachum. I've made up my mind. I'm leaving school. I am going to the Army." I blurt out a string of proclamations.

For a moment Mom is silent. Then, without taking her eyes off the road, she says, "You're not cut out for the Army. You need to stay home, change your major to nursing. You'll like that better than Psychology, anyway. You would be good in nursing."

"You don't even know me, do you? I would fucking suck as a nurse." I stare out the window at the flat landscape now buckling into rolling hills. "I'm good at the Army, hooah."

"Hooah." She purses her lips, drawing out the word to mock me. "F-this and F-that. I can't believe you're my daughter." She checks the rearview and moves into the fast lane.

"Feeling's mutual," I say. "That's one reason I'm going to Europe with the Army."

"If you think you can go to the Army and live in Europe, then you're suffering from delusions of grandeur. I recognize these symptoms from my psych rotation in nursing school."

"Look who's got delusions of grandeur. You have just about as much training as I do after my one Intro Psych class."

"Well, I'm also your mother and I see you have a problem. Instead of going to the recruiter when we get back, you need to go to a psych unit."

"Bullshit. The only unit I'm going to is my Reserve unit." Wiping the spit dripping down my chin, I know I'm not making a great case. "You're my problem. You and that town."

"You're not in your right mind." Mom tucks a twig of her Clairol ash-blond hair behind her ear. "I will be in Kentucky when the Army calls from Germany. I can't help you when they say they found you confused on the *Autobahn*, and you've forgotten who you are."

"I can only pray that I forget who I am," I shout from across the car. "I wish I could forget everything about my life, this world. But I doubt I'll suddenly enter into a fugue state."

"You're nineteen." She grips the steering wheel. Her dark-tinted, freshly manicured nails, a rare splurge just for my brother's

Army graduation, dig into her palms. "The same age as your dad's other daughter, when she..." Mom pauses, then continues. "Your father broke your sister. He broke her mother, his first wife, too. He couldn't break me. But you're not like me. You take after your dad's side. Eventually he would have broken you. And the Army will break you."

"I can't be broken." Resting my chin in the web between my thumb and forefinger, I snicker. "I survived my father for ten years, remember? And I lived with you for eighteen. If you two couldn't break me, the Army sure as hell can't."

On her left ring finger, Mom adjusts the old wedding set her new husband bought her down at the pawn shop. He was her first love when she was eighteen. She still defends him and his choice to go AWOL before he shipped out to the war in Vietnam. Once, during an argument I called him a traitor to his country. Now he and Mom won't let me back into the house where I grew up.

"I won't always be here to look after you," she says. "That's why I'm telling you to find yourself a good man now."

"I've always taken care of myself. I've pretty much been on my own since I went to the Army. I don't suddenly need some man." I spy a mile-marker. I glance at the speedometer, then the clock. I do the mental math, calculating how many more hours I have left in this car.

"You're one of those weak women," she says, her eyes narrowing on the road in front of us.

"When I rucked two-thirds of my body weight on a twelve-hour march, when a two-hundred-pound drill sergeant screamed in my face, when I drove twenty-thousand-pound trucks through the mud, I didn't crack—I smiled. The Army showed me how strong I really am."

"I should have never let you take your brother to the recruiter. I should have never let you join, neither one of you."

"Let me? You practically sold me to the recruiter for some

magic beans. Then you told me to take my brother to the recruiting office. You said the Army would do him good, like me."

"Well, I was mistaken. I thought it changed you for the better, but I should have seen what was staring me in the face. After you came back home from Basic, you were not a normal girl. You didn't act like all my friends' girls your age. The Army ruined you."

"You're right." I blink away hot tears. "The Army did ruin me. I'll never be a 'normal girl'," I said, making air-quotes with my fingers. "I'll never be the sweet, pretty, blonde, all-American girl next door who wants to get married and have babies. I don't know what you thought the Army is like, but they trained me to be a soldier, not a girl scout. There is a world out there and I want to experience it before I die. I'm sorry if I can't be who you want me to be."

Mom chews the inside of her cheek. "Yeah, well, I'm sorry, too."

"And you were right about another thing. I am about to break. I will break if I don't get away from you and the life you are forcing me to live." The tears stream down my face before I can catch them. "I'm putting an ocean between me and you and this life you want me to live. The Atlantic isn't big enough, but I guess it will have to do."

I end the chapter of my past year and close the book on my life for now. I am back in my English classroom, standing in front of the lectern. Professor Harris looks at me.

"So?" he asks. "I know what's in it for the Army, but what's in it for you?"

I do not know how to give him a simplified version of the truth, but I attempt.

"Europe," I say. "The Army's promised me a duty station in Europe."

"Europe is a big place, you know? They can put you anywhere."

"I know." I shrug. "It doesn't matter to me, so long as I go to Europe."

"Kosovo is in Europe. There's a war there. Our government doesn't like to recognize certain conflicts as war, but they are. What if you go there?"

"I know." I bite my lip. "Well, if I go I go. I'm not afraid to fight."

"That's it? You're trading your life to the Army for that?" He hangs his head. "The Army will use you up and throw you away. Have you not been paying attention in this class?"

I consider telling Doctor, Professor, Lieutenant, or whoever Harris that the world might end tomorrow or it might go on forever, but I can't live one more moment like this. I would die for a moment of real life, I think. I want a life like you or Tim O'Brien with stories worth writing about.

"My mind is made up. Sir." I straighten myself into a tall, stiff soldier posture.

My professor writes my name beside some notes in his book.

CHAPTER 3

BLUE BIRD

Days into a new year, a new month, a new millennium in an ancient land, far from the hills of Kentucky, a blue bird cuts a path through the frosty mid-morning air. It brings on its tail clouds spitting snow, anxiety floating atop buzzcuts and buns, and a future folded like a topographical map. Instead of chirping or humming or the sound of wings fluttering, the bird roars, squelches, then gasps as it lands in front of the crowd gathering on the sidewalk.

The canary yellow of its body, the color I was accustomed to seeing as a school girl, is replaced with a muted tan. Other than the silhouette of a flying bird painted on its side and the words Blue Bird stamped into the front, there are no markings. When I see it is not colored OD Green or tattooed with the U.S. Army logo like in the movies, I swallow some mild disappointment. The Blue Bird bus will do its job, without thanks, without notice, and camouflage the weary soldiers in its belly as it moves across the Rhineland.

My orders say the Blue Bird will carry me far from anything I have ever known. Already I have traveled two weeks via buses, cars, and planes, across land masses, mountains, and even the Atlantic just to begin my journey. Now, I will leave the in-processing station here at Rhine-Main and join my company, 420th Quartermasters. I will leave the Frankfurt area in central Germany with its bustling nightlife, museums, and operas and head to Verner Barracks in a small town I've never heard of, called Bimbleberg, in Bavaria.

It seems a cruel twist of fate that I should be plucked from my Podunk town with its one Christian Bookstore and a Walmart only to be set down in the middle of nowhere Bum-Fuck Europe. None of the military personnel working at Rhine-Main could tell me much about my new town. I asked if it was a good unit, if it was a good duty station. The Airman handing me my orders said, "The military is what you make it."

After two hours of passing empty vineyards, quaint houses with red roofs, and uninterpretable *Autobahn* signage, we drive through city streets and roll to a stop outside a gate guarded by two tall fit men wearing blue uniforms. They speak in German to the driver. I stand up to look out the opposite side of the bus. "Are we here? Is this it?" I ask the soldier I nearly crush in my efforts to peer outside.

She says nothing. I search for a billboard, a marker, anything. Then I see it. On a red brick perfect rectangle of a sign with sharp ninety-degree angles written in a white, no-frills font are the words "United States Army Verner Barracks". The uniformed guards wave the driver through and stare through each window.

"We're here," I say. "But why does the Army need civilian guards?" Through the window, I make eye contact with one of the uniformed men. I hold on to the back of the seat as the bus gives me a jolt. "Are they here to keep us in or someone else out?" I laugh at this line I must have lifted from a movie, but the soldier looks unimpressed and continues staring straight ahead.

When the Blue Bird pulls to a stop and opens the doors,

soldiers file out without a word, as if operating under silent command. I follow their lead. A single cobblestone, one of many that forms the street, rolls under the weight of my spit-shined, black Kiwi-ed combat boot as I step off the bus. Germany feels old and steeped in fable. Even the word "cobblestone" sounds as if it belongs to a time and place found only in storybooks. My left ankle gives way with a piece of the street. The only injury is to my pride since I, like all soldiers, lace my boots tighter than a virgin's corset. I straighten my back inside my heavy field jacket, bracing myself against the shock of the frigid January air. I walk on, hoping no one noticed.

Behind me I hear a deep voice call out, "Here in Germany, you got to always be looking where you walk." Over my shoulder I see a man, barely out of his teenage years. I observe the buck sergeant stripes in the middle of his camo Gore-Tex jacket. He speaks like a man who knows his shit, like someone who has been here and seen all this before.

"Got to watch your step in this place." The young sergeant steps over to my side and pushes the loose stone back in place. "Specialist Burton?" he cocks his head, noting the insignia on my collar and my name embroidered on the right breast of my coat. "You got to be careful. It's not like back home. These streets are dangerous. I've seen a lot of soldiers really get hurt over here."

The silvery clouds break and I feel the sun's warmth on my face. I lift my eyes to see the Army base glowing in all its homogenous glory. In the waning daylight, rows of beige stucco buildings glow. None taller than three stories, not counting the little dormer windows jutting out of the black pitched roofs. I overhear a soldier say, "Those must be the barracks."

The buildings look more like Cold War prison barracks instead of billets for U.S. soldiers. Except for those of us who are disembarking from the bus, the whole place feels deserted. Unlike the bigger bases of Ft. Leonard Wood or Ft. Lee, there is no traffic, no cars going to Burger King after duty, no soldiers headed for a beer after a long day. The base was engineered with what soldiers would need to perform their duties in mind. The small buildings loom large and block out the sinking sun. Their windows grow dark and their stucco facades threaten to encase me.

"There will be someone from your new company to pick you up. If you're lucky that is," a bulky loud mouth buck sergeant shouts at those of us who have gathered our belongings from the bus. I try to figure out who he is, and the best I can tell, he has been sent to wrangle all the newcomers. Waving some papers in the air, he laughs, "But for those of you who ain't so lucky, here's some maps. You'll be rucking to your new units."

A low rumbling emanates from the crowd. Someone mutters, "Well, ain't that some Army bullshit." A few soldiers seem to know their destiny, and pick up the maps. With their pregnant duffle bags slung over their shoulders, they start off down the post. Others, the lucky ones, I suppose, hop into Humvees or Deuce-and-a-Half trucks with a Specialist or other lower-enlisted soldier at the wheel. Still some lucky bastards or highly ranked individuals get carted off by a uniformed soldier in a privately owned vehicle.

For a moment I let myself hope I might be lucky enough due to my rank of Specialist to get a ride in a Humvee or thrown in the back of a truck along with some other cargo. Then I remind myself I am in the Army and there is no such thing as a free ride. I search the thinning crowd for someone who might be my ride. I at last give up and take a map, some Xerox copy of a copy of a copy of the base. I turn it upside down and around, trying to figure out which direction to ruck to get to my new unit, but I am as lost as a newly pinned lieutenant straight out of ROTC.

Picking up my Army duffel bag, which weighs about as much as I do, I stand it on its bottom. It comes up to my chest. I locate my tweed garment bag from K-mart that carries my Class A dress uniform. How professional I thought I would feel and look carrying a garment bag on international travel. Now, however, I'm bogged down under the weight of everything as I sling it over my right shoulder and strap my duffel on my back like a rucksack. According to what I work out from the map, it must be at least half a mile in the frigid temps under my unwieldy gear to my company's HQ. I tell myself to suck it up, buttercup, when a man shouts, "Burton? Is there a Specialist Burton here?"

I turn to see a tall, reed-thin sergeant who looks to be about a hard thirty. On his lanky frame the creases of his starched, thick cold-weather BDUs form jagged angles. His back forms an almost scoliotic curve, causing his head to line up with the toes of his boots. I wonder if God or the Army cursed him with that spine.

I wave, "I'm Burton, Sergeant." He smiles a bucktoothed grin and his brown eyes warm as if he recognizes me.

"I'm Sergeant Samuels," he says. "Sergeant Bluff's your platoon sergeant, but I'm his number two guy at the 420th SSA."

"Hi, I'm Specialist Burton, Sergeant." He grabs my garment bag off my shoulder and I do some mental gymnastics, recalling from training that SSA stands for Supply Support Activity. I'm not sure what that translates to in civilian language and I don't want to show my ignorance by asking, so I hope I'm right in assuming it's where the Army keeps its supplies.

"Did you think you were going to have to ruck?" He shines his two big front teeth at me. He nods toward the guys walking with their gear. "Look at those poor dumb fucks. I'll never understand as long as I'm in the Army why their platoon sergeants can't send someone to get them." He watches them as they walk. "Well, it's all part of the game."

"Game?"

"Yeah," he replies. "They're artillery. That's what they do in those all-male companies. They want to treat those lower-enlisted guys like shit as soon as they get here. Kind of haze them, you know?"

"Oh, I see."

"But that's not how we do things in the Four-Twenty."

"Right, Sergeant," I laugh, "I guess I'm lucky, huh? Y'all sent a platoon sergeant down here to get me even though I'm just a Specialist."

"That's right." He motions toward a blue, mid-eighties BMW sedan. "We take care of our soldiers. Wait until you see the barracks. We've assigned you to one of the big rooms with no roommates since you're one of the higher-ranking soldiers we've got living there."

"Wow."

"Yep," he says. "We like to do things correct."

As we walk toward a blue mid-eighties BMW, I stop and stare. My mouth drops open.

"Is that your car, Sergeant?" I ask.

"Uh-huh," he says.

"Whoa. That's a nice car, Sergeant."

Sergeant Samuels cocks an eyebrow. "Yeah, it's all right for a third-hand old Beamer." I unshoulder my duffel and toss it in the trunk alongside my garment bag. "It's starting to rust, and it's impossible to keep clean with Germany's rain. I don't even bother washing it anymore. But it'll do while I'm stationed here."

"No, Sergeant, this is great." My eyes widen as large as the BMW medallion on the back. I plop into the passenger side and all the questions I wanted to ask about Germany, my comrades, and the unit fly out of my head. I am rendered mute, but I can't stop looking around. I want to remember every detail of this moment, the first time I ever sat in a luxury German vehicle. I ignore the hole in the console with licking tongues of wires, reaching for a stereo long gone, the stained, balding carpet of the floorboards, and the odd aroma of cigarettes mixing with mildew. Instead, I focus on the five-speed stick shift, which whispers to me accounts of speeding on a highway system limited only by driver and car, not law enforcement. From its place in the center of the steering wheel the blue eye of the Bavarian Motor Works logo winks at me.

"You know," Sergeant Samuels says, "You could get a Beamer too."

"I don't know, Sergeant. I'm just a Specialist."

"Even broke-ass Privates drive BMWs over here. It's too expensive for Germans to upgrade these old cars to meet these new emissions standards, but that doesn't apply to us. You can find a 1980s Beamer or Mercedes pretty cheap." He rubs his hands over the steering wheel, then lightly strokes the shifter. "Almost every German car is a manual. Can you drive a stick?"

"Hell, yeah. Here on Active duty I'm a Ninety-Two Alpha Logistical Specialist, but I was an Eighty-Eight Mike truck driver in the Reserves." The words pour out. Regaining my military bearing, I say. "I mean, yes, Sergeant. They taught me in training to handle just about everything the Army's got."

Sergeant Samuels chuckles and turns the key. He shifts through first, second, then third. Like a little blue bird, the car flutters along. It hums down one-way cobblestone streets and blind corners, leaving self-doubt and the past crumpled up like a useless street map behind on the ground.

CHAPTER 4

LIVE, LOVE, DRIVE

In the stars of the frosty Bavarian January evening, she twinkles. The moon shines down only on her, leaving the others cloaked in darkness. She sits perched on a knoll, just above the rest. Even in the sunlight earlier in the day, when I caught my first glimpse, she was no less magnificent. It is as if the heavenly bodies are no more immune from looking at her than we mortals.

To gaze upon such a magnificent piece of German engineering —a silver, mid-80s, 3-series BMW—fills me with emotions and ideas I've never felt before. My heart races in her presence. I long to make her mine. Her sleek body and low profile make her beautiful, but they also make her fast. She shows off four fat tires sure to grip the *Autobahn*, and inside she has a small, thick steering wheel designed for racing. Her price tag tells me she is a little too good for someone of my rank.

My buddy, also a Specialist, who everyone calls Low because they say his full name is too long to pronounce, works with me in Shipping and Receiving in the back of the SSA. He has come with me tonight to marvel at this beauty. He and Specialist Dale, who I also work with in the back, have become my two new best friends.

After watching both soldiers race their BMWs up The Hill every morning to the warehouse, I struck up a conversation with them about their cars. They regaled me with stories about driving a hundred miles an hour down the *Autobahn* and a crash in which Low flipped his last car upside down only to crawl across two lanes of traffic to retrieve his CD player. After hearing such tales I knew theirs was a fraternity I had to pledge. Like me, I knew they were all about experiencing everything in life. I told them I was in the market for a used German car and asked for any advice they could offer a newbie, like me.

Down here at the Lemon Lot, so called because this is the place where soldiers put their old BMWs, Mercedes, and Porsches for sale before shipping back to The States, I swear to my buddy and myself that I am only window-shopping. Low doesn't believe me, I suspect, because I don't even believe me. I like to credit myself with being a rational person. I mull over every decision, thinking through the pros and cons and every potential outcome, but I feel I have lost my heart and my head to this car. Maybe I want Low to be the rational angel on my shoulder and bring me back to my senses. Or maybe I want him to be the devil on the other shoulder. I want him to tell me I should do this wild and crazy thing because I already did a wild and crazy thing—left home and came to Germany.

Low and I walk the row of cars lined up like soldiers in formation under the streetlights. Like drill sergeants inspecting their troops we size each one up, pointing out flaws. The white Ford hatchback is too slow and looks like a dirty egg. The large, pastel Mercedes is for some dad chauffeuring his kids around base on the weekend. Then we stop at the BMW, my BMW.

"Oh," I say, as if noticing it for the first time. "This one is nice. What do you think?"

Low walks his lanky figure to the front of the car and surveys the vehicle. "Looks nice."

The paper taped to the rear passenger side window lists features like new sport tires and racing steering wheel.

"Hmm," he says. "How much?"

"Kind of a lot," I giggle.

He walks to my side and eyeballs the paper. "Too much."

"Yeah, but, I mean, the seller might negotiate. Right?"

"A little, I guess." He shrugs his lean shoulders. "But that's too much for a 1985 BMW."

"Is it?" I stare at the paper. "It says the brakes were just replaced. And the tires are brand new."

"Meh." Low walks back up the row to check out a newer 5-series we just passed. "There are a lot of old Beamers. Look at this one. They're not asking anything close to that one."

"I saw that one," I say, my feet still planted by the silver car. "It looks like it's been driven hard. And it doesn't have the upgrades like this one."

"They've all been driven hard," Low says. "And I don't know why someone would put all those things on a car that they are only going to own for a couple of years. It seems like a waste of money."

"I don't know," I say. "The same thing has been said about you and Dale and your Beamers."

"That's different." His voice grows firm. "Me and Dale didn't spend a lot of money on our cars."

"Well." I dig into my pocket for my phone. "There's only one way to know what this car's story is. I'm going to call about it."

Low shakes his head. "What do you want to do?"

"I didn't say I was going to buy it." I look up from the keypad. "I just said I was going to call."

He rolls his eyes.

"Besides," I tilt my head up at the night sky, "I'll probably just get voicemail, anyway. It's already after final formation and dinner chow."

With the numbers punched in, I hit send and put the phone to my ear. After a few rings, a male German voice on the other end answers, "Hallo?"

Fifteen minutes later, an older beige Mercedes lumbers into the parking lot, spotlighting my buddy and me as if we are two deer in the woods. Someone cuts the engine, killing the lights. A middle-aged man with thinning blond hair blown around his crown gets out of the driver's side. He is wearing a fair-isle sweater, thick wool socks pulled over jeans, and boots. Smiling, he waves as if we his are best friends. "Gruss Gott," he says in a deep voice, giving Low and me the traditional southern German greeting. I can't decide if this guy is the epitome of Bavarian friendliness or if he has escaped from a nearby facility to come murder us.

From the passenger side, a woman with the same wild, thinning hair as the man steps out to the front of the car. She is tall and sturdy, similar in features to the driver. I wonder if she is his wife or sister or even mother. She has on ill-fitting blue jeans, shearling-lined clogs, and no make-up. She hugs her down winter coat tight against her body.

"Gruss Gott," she says, and her eyes crinkle at the corners. She looks older than she sounded on the phone. "I am Gertrud. This is my brother, Peter. He doesn't speak much English."

Peter smiles and waves again.

"This is my buddy, Low," I say. "I'm Burton."

"Nice to meet you." She shakes hands with me, then Low.

"Is this your car?" I ask, unsure if she is the owner or the translator. The "For Sale" paper in the window listed a phone number, but no name. Neither she nor her brother look like someone I imagined would own a sporty BMW.

"Yes." Her eyes look up and then off to the right. "Well, it was my husband's. It is mine now."

"Oh," I say.

"So you said on the phone you would like some information on the auto. What would you like to know?"

"Well, uh." I stare at her like a deer in VW headlights. I assumed she would arrive and start talking up the car. "Um, well, just some general things, I guess. Whatever you might want to tell me."

Darting my eyes over at Low, I hope he'll get the message and jump in with some questions. For all my interest in cars, I have never really shopped for one. While I was in Basic Mom informed me she would find a car for me. She said I was too inexperienced and didn't know how to make good decisions for myself, so she would do it for me. I just needed to write a check. After a long day in Basic, before I drifted off to sleep in my bunk, I imagined cruising the town in a small used convertible, still good on gas. I would straddle the line between practical, yet fun with my car choice.

When I came home, parked next to hers, was a car in the same make, model, year, and color as hers—a red, 1990 Pontiac Grand Am. She smiled, expecting me to excited. My face dropped. The car was not at all what we agreed she would purchase for me, I said. When I asked her why she got me a "mom car", she dropped the keys at my feet. She claimed I didn't appreciate anything she did for me. Without her help to make the right decisions, she said, I would ruin my life. Not only was I naïve, but I wasn't "quite right". She said I would always need her to help me, to look after me, and that I would never make it in the world on my own.

Before I went off to Basic Training, she said the same thing. I thought she would have had more faith in my abilities once I came home a soldier at seventeen, with money and a plan to take care of myself after high school like she wanted, but a year later when I went to college, then when I chose my major, and again before I left for Germany she told me I was incapable of taking care of myself.

Standing here on the Lemon Lot, I feel the weight of it all. I worry Mom is right about everything. I worry I've made a horrible mistake coming here or that I'll ruin my life now that I am left to make my own decisions. I wonder if I should call Mom and ask her what I should do.

No, I decide. I am a soldier. I am a grown woman. This is what I wanted.

I listen as Gertrud rambles off the specs like a used car dealer. She's even come prepared with a copy of the same "For Sale" fact sheet that was taped to the car.

"Hmm-hmm." I look at the page. My mind blanks. All I can remember is advice from relatives, friends, and TV shows saying a car buyer should never look too eager.

"You can see the price, here." She points at the amount in Deutschmarks listed at the bottom. "It's fair for such a good car. My husband made lots of improvements."

"Yes." I look up from the page. I maintain a flat, uninterested voice. "It might be more than I'm looking to spend, though. This is the first car I've really looked at..."

"We can drive it," she says. "You can see it is better than these other cars for sale here. My husband was an Army mechanic. He always took good care of it."

"Maybe I'll have a better look at it before I drive it. Can you open it up, so I can look under the hood and inside?"

She opens the driver's side door and pops the hood. "After that we drive it."

Low and I walk to the front and raise the hood. We lean under the hood. I whisper, "It looks like a decent car, I mean with new brakes, new tires. And she says the guy was a mechanic. What do you think about it?"

"I don't know. It's up to you," he says.

"Well." I tap on the windshield washer reservoir. "I don't have a damn clue what I'm looking at."

"I don't know either." He hangs his head and laughs.

"What the hell, Low?" I chuckle. "You're supposed to be helping me."

"I never even drove a car before I came to Germany." He pulls his head out from under the hood. "I didn't even have my license back in the States. The soldier who sold me my first car taught me so I would buy his car."

"Wow." My eyes widen. "That's incredible. Well, you're a hell of a driver now. Except for that time you crashed on the *Autobahn*."

"That was not my fault."

"Yeah, uh-uh." I nudge him in the side with my elbow. "Seriously, though. This lady wants me to test drive this thing tonight. I have never driven in Germany. What if I crash her car?"

"That's on her."

"Shit." I pat down the cargo pockets of my BDUs. "I didn't even bring my glasses." Wearing glasses is a sign of weakness in the Army. When in uniform, I only wear them while driving or on the range.

"Just tell her you don't want to drive it tonight."

"Okay." I look out from over the hood for Gertrud and Peter. "That's what I'll do."

After pulling on some hoses and tugging on some lines, I walk back to where the brother and sister are standing.

"What do you think?" Gertrud asks.

"Yeah," I nod, "looks nice. I think I need some time, but thank you..."

"You haven't driven it yet," she says. "You can't decide before you drive."

"It's getting kind of late." I look at my friend, then at my watch. "We really need to get back to the barracks. We have an early formation."

"I know what time formation is," she smiles. "I was married to a soldier. You have time for a drive."

I turn to Low and sigh.

"C'mon." She holds the key out. "You and I take the car for a drive. The men can stay here."

The key and infinite possibility dangle before me. My practical side gives way under the weight of Gertrud's persuasion. I take the key, jump in the driver's seat, and allow my hands to caress the thick steering wheel.

She takes her seat beside me. "That is real leather."

"Wow, really?"

My right hand finds its place on the shifter. I put my feet on the brake and clutch, then turn the key. My heart jumps into my throat as the engine roars to life.

"It sounds good, doesn't it?" Gertrud yells over the sound of the engine.

I wave out the windshield at Low.

"Where should we take it?" I ask.

"We can go out Gate Three and make a right. There are some good roads out of town. No lights."

"You want to go off-post?"

"You have your driver's license, yes?"

"Yes, but..."

"Then you'll be fine. Let's go."

I wonder who's crazier, Gertrud or me. Because I have a state driver's license, all I had to do to get a United States Army Europe driver's license was pass a paper test. I didn't even have to get behind the wheel and prove I could drive in Germany. I question if I'm qualified to be doing this. Despite my misgivings about my ability to operate a motor vehicle in a foreign country, or about driving without my glasses, or even about getting into a car at night with a stranger, I still do all these things. Maybe Mom was right. I don't belong out on my own, making decisions for myself.

I push the thoughts aside to focus on my tach and speedometer, careful not to get a kilometer above the base's speed limit. As soon as we pass the guard shack of Gate 3 and are no longer subject to the prying eyes of the military police, Gertrud says, "Okay, now you can open it up a little."

Out of the corner of my right eye, I glance over at her. I never imagined someone telling me to "open it up".

I shift into third. I zip along the street that hugs the base's perimeter. On the left, old Army barracks whir by. We make a right, a left, and another right until we are somewhere outside of the city limits. We are into some deep darkness I believe exists only in Kentucky or Army field sites. The car follows its headlights around tight corners and up rolling hills. In the dark winter night, inky trees shiver. My hands grip the wheel and I squint to bring the world into focus. One wrong move could send me into one of those trees or off the shoulder.

"You can drive faster," Gertrud says, relaxing into her seat. "You are only in third gear." "Yeah." I touch my palm to the shifter, contemplating speeding up. "I would if it were my car."

"Why don't you pull over up here?"

At a wide spot to the side of the road I ease the car over. My palms are drenched in sweat. I wipe them on my trousers. Except for the car, there is nothing but silence. All of nature must be tucked in somewhere warm. I wish I too were safe in my bed back in the barracks instead of out here with this strange German lady.

"What do you think?" she asks.

"It's nice." I bob my head. "And it's pretty. It seems like a nice car."

"It goes fast." Her voice lilts.

"Yeah, I'm sure it does."

"You like to drive?" she asks, almost prodding, "You like driving fast in America?"

"Yes," I smile as I think back to another time. "I used to drive trucks in the Army. Before I came here. I work in a warehouse now, so I don't think I'll get to drive much anymore."

"You must be a good driver if the Army taught you."

"I'm okay, I guess. I liked it. I really miss driving."

She tilts her head to one shoulder and smiles. I guess her to be about Mom's age and I try to imagine Mom driving a car like this.

"You said this was your husband's car?" I ask.

"Oh, yes." She looks out the passenger's side window while picking at something on the armrest. "He loved this car. He said he always wanted a BMW, but they cost too much in America. We never had kids, so he called it his baby."

"Oh. Yeah," I say. "What rank is your husband?"

"He was a sergeant."

"Was?" I ask. "Is he out of the Army? Are you selling so you can go back to the States?"

"Yes, well." She turns to gaze out ahead. "He is going back. I'm not going with him."

I look at her, puzzled.

"We are getting a divorce." She turns to me. "I get to keep the car, but I need to sell it because it doesn't meet German environmental standards. It is okay for American soldiers to have dirty cars, but not for German citizens."

"Oh." I nod and look away. "Right."

"That's okay." Her voice rises, like she wants to believe what she says. "These things happen in the Army. The Army is hard on families."

"Yeah, that's what I hear." My palms still feel sweaty, so I wipe them again.

"Was that your husband or boyfriend with you?"

"Low? No. He's my buddy. No, I'm single. Just my mom back home."

"I bet she misses you, but it's probably not so hard on you to leave her to come here to Germany. Children are supposed to grow up and leave their families."

"Well," I let out a nervous laugh. "I don't think my leaving was too hard on either one of us."

Pointing outside the windshield, Gertrud says. "Let's go out on the *Autobahn*." I make out a sign for the *Autobahn* on-ramp looming just ahead of us.

"Right now? It's getting kind of late. Maybe we should get back to base."

"We're not far from the Kaserne. We won't be long."

Dropping my head, I let out an audible sigh. "I don't know about driving on the *Autobahn*."

"You don't want to?"

Given the opportunity to at last realize my dream of racing down the *Autobahn*, I am suddenly paralyzed with anxiety. This is not how I imagined I'd react if I ever saw this day. Driving felt so natural that I joked it was encoded on my DNA, passed down from both sides of my family.

It isn't just this drive, though. Since coming to Germany, I have second-guessed everything about myself. Sometimes I have bursts of self-confidence, only to have them punctured by self-doubt. I can hear Mom's words, my own words telling me I am some idiot child unequipped for the world. But when I saw myself as the badass driver, the funny friend, the good soldier, I could hear another part of me saying, "That's not the real you."

"I want to drive on the *Autobahn*." I stare out into space. "I just..."

"What is wrong? You know how to drive."

"Yes, no..." I run my fingers around the circumference of the steering wheel. "I mean, I can drive in the States. I don't know how to drive on the *Autobahn*."

"You know how to drive on the *Autobahn*. It's the same as in the States."

She leans further back in the seat.

I start the car and say a silent prayer. Oh, God. Don't let me fuck this up.

The reflective white highway icon of the *Autobahn* sign glows like neon in the headlights. I turn right onto the ramp. In the low gear the engine revs, urging me to shift. I give it some gas, and shift. Checking my rearview, my side view, I change gears into fourth. In a split second, the car launches onto the *Autobahn*.

"Woah." I glance at Gertrud to see if she notices we made the jump into hyperspace. I shift into fifth. Red tail lights appear in front of me. I move to the fast lane to overtake the car. "Ha!" I look in my rearview. "Did you see that? It looks like he's just sitting there."

She laughs.

Other cars in front of me see me approaching and get out of my way. They seem to bow in subservience as I pass them all one by one.

"Holy shit," I read the speedometer. "I'm going like a hundred and fifty kilometers an hour."

"I told you it was fast." Gertrud throws her head back.

My face hurts from grinning. I ease into a comfortable cruising speed and lean back into the seat. From behind the wheel, things look different. At twenty years old, after a little over two years, I have risen through several ranks to Specialist in the United States Army when Mom said I would never make it through Basic. I have traveled to Germany, where my sergeants have assigned me to a big room all to myself. Less than two months ago my roommate and I were arguing about buying toilet paper. Tonight, who I was or who people said I was in Kentucky fades into a black and white memory as I become someone new, someone who does things like drive BMWs on the *Autobahn*.

I change lanes, letting a new Mercedes pass. Up ahead a sign for a town with an unpronounceable name announces its distance in kilometers. It is a new world, but it feels right. The car, my car —I have decided—floats down the *Autobahn*. It is as if I could drive all night. I no longer care how far from home or base I've strayed or about getting enough sleep for first formation tomorrow. I am awake. I am in love. I am alive. Moonlight mingles with headlights and the future is luminescent.

Chapter 5

The Performance

Like mice, soldiers scurry and hide in the corners of the front section of the warehouse. Quiet drapes itself like a curtain over everyone and everything in the section. The moment I cross through the threshold of the double doors from my section in the rear into the front I feel the difference. I have left behind the humming forklifts and chattering soldiers in the back of the warehouse. Only the sound of papers shuffling on desks and clicking of fingers on keyboards breaks the stillness. It's the sound of busy work. Already, I resent those who work up front at computers and desks. They think themselves smarter than us in the back. But to us they are snobs. They don't understand how much we juggle—both mentally and physically—in our positions.

No one looks up at me as I make my way to Sergeant Bluff's office at the font of the warehouse. It's the sight of soldiers who think if they don't see they won't be seen. It is early February, and I have been here for only a few weeks. Already, though, I understand that when a soldier is called to the office, he or she must have done something to make them a bad soldier. Afraid my sins might rub off on them, the soldiers divert their gaze from me.

Sergeant Bluff's office is flanked on either side by the Lieutenant's and Sergeant Samuels's. Built up on a sort of platform,
the three offices sit up and off the warehouse floor. Constructed of
cheap plywood barely hanging in their frames, the doors remind
me of background props on a college theater stage.

Sunlight beaming through Sergeant Bluff's door, which hangs
ajar, pierces my pupils. Coming out of the darkness of the back of
the warehouse I realize I haven't seen daylight since yesterday. I
also realize that dancing at the German *disko* with Low and Dale
until 0400 hours this morning was not the best decision of my life.

I pause and take in a deep breath, trying to calm my stage fright.
I must go forward, knock, and report and pretend to be this character, this soldier who knows what the hell she is doing. I swallow hard
and knock on the door. The Reserves weren't big on military
customs, like saluting or even reporting. I try to recall the procedures
and pray if I get them wrong I will be forgiven. It is as if mold has
grown over my brain and my ears buzz like flies with each thought.
It might be due to nerves or the leftover beats of last night's techno.

The adrenaline rushes to my head and my hands shake. Dirty
boot prints in front of the platform mark where another soldier
once stood. I slide my feet into them. The prints surround my
boots on either side and I am reminded of my smallness. Through
the noise I hear the low tone of a male voice. I can't make out the
words, but I assume it is Sergeant Bluff, telling me to come in. I
push the door open the rest of the way, hoping I guessed right.

Behind a heavy wooden desk Sergeant Bluff sits with his back
to the windows. To his immediate left, Sergeant Samuels is
standing at his side. I stand in the doorway, look up at the ceiling
for my script. "Sergeant Bluff, Specialist Burton reporting."

Sergeant Samuels grins and shakes his head at me. He and
Sergeant Bluff laugh, but I don't get what's so funny. Sergeant
Samuels moves from behind the desk and pulls a chair out towards

the middle of the room. He goes behind me and closes the door. Still laughing, he says, "You can relax, Burton, it's not that formal of a meeting."

I clasp my hands into the small of my back into some hybrid version of parade rest and at ease, since I am not sure just how informal we are talking.

"Why don't you have a seat, right here." Sergeant Samuels nods at the black banquet chair he's pulled out from the side of the wall. "Me and Sergeant Bluff just want to have a talk with you."

Sergeant Bluff moves out from behind his desk and hovers over my five-foot-four frame. He stands at least eight feet tall and as broad-shouldered as a lumberjack. He is the U.S. Army personified. He makes Uncle Sam wish he could have had sons. In the black mirrors of his combat boots, I see the reflection of a disappointment, a daughter.

"I didn't bring a battle buddy, Sergeants." I grip my hands tight behind my back. "I can run to the back and get Low or Dale."

"That's not necessary." Sergeant Bluff and Sergeant Samuels pull up a couple of chairs. "You don't need a battle buddy. We're just going to have a conversation."

They take their seats and motion at an empty chair in front of them. I sit opposite the two men and force an uneasy smile. As is the custom in the Army to sit at attention, I put my palms on the tops of my thighs and plant my feet firmly into the floor.

"Relax, Burton," Sergeant Bluff grins. "We just want to talk." I relax my back against the chair. "How do you like the Four-Twentieth so far? You like it up here with us at the SSA?"

"Yes, Sergeant." I smile at him, then over at Sergeant Samuels. "I like it here."

"Good, good." Sergeant Bluff nods. "Glad to hear it. And how do you like the barracks? You know I'm in charge of the barracks, so if you have any complaints you can come to me."

"No, Sergeant, no complaints. They're nice."

"Sergeant Samuels got you settled in, he said, when you first arrived. He got you put up in one of the big rooms, didn't you Sergeant Samuels?"

"I sure did, Sergeant Bluff." Sergeant Samuels looks over to his right at Sergeant Bluff, who still smiles at me.

"How do you like that room? We usually keep those for sergeants, but if there are some empties we give them to some Specialists. It's nice, huh?"

"Yes, Sergeant. It's a bigger room than I expected."

"I'm sure you've seen how some of the other soldiers have made their rooms pretty nice, am I right? Do you know what I'm talking about?" He lowers his head and looks up under his eyebrows.

"Yes, Sergeant, I've seen a couple."

"So you're getting it all fixed up, then?"

"Sergeant?"

"Well, me and Sergeant Samuels saw you the other day, walking from the PX carrying a whole bunch of stuff, didn't we Sergeant Samuels?"

"Oh, yeah." Sergeant Samuels's buck teeth jut through his smile. "You were carrying all kinds of things back to the barracks. You had bags of stuff and you were bear-hugging what looked like stuff for your bed. Why didn't you just put that thing on your back and ruck it, Burton?" He laughs, but soon drops the smile. He leans back in his chair and crosses his arms. There's a long pause. I scrunch up my face as my platoon sergeants stare at me. I attempt to answer, but then hesitate.

"You had someone with you, didn't you? You had someone helping you carry all that stuff?" Sergeant Bluff asks.

I stare at him, then down at the floor and try to choose my

next words carefully. I remember how another soldier told me all about the Better Opportunity for Single Soldiers, aka BOSS, program that allows soldiers to decorate their barracks rooms with civilian items, like TVs with surround sound, stereo systems with towering speakers, even posters and pictures hanging on the walls. With only a small boombox on loan from another soldier on the desk, a silver scrolled frame holding a photo of my best friend and me on the nightstand, and a burgundy floral bedspread on my bed, my room is modest compared to many. Some of the other soldiers' rooms look as if they belong to Private Hugh Hefner, GI, of the Playboy Barracks. Overstuffed black leather couches and chairs, glass coffee tables with gold-accented tusk feet, zebra-skinned rugs, and fully stocked mirrored bars are not uncommon.

"You had another soldier with you." Sergeant Bluff shifts forward, leaning in closer to me. "Who was he, Burton? I didn't recognize him. He wasn't one of ours. Was he your boyfriend?"

I zone out and focus on a piece of wall straight in front of me, between Sergeant Samuels and Sergeant Bluff. The real estate of yellow, dingy drywall is broken up by smudgy gray fingerprints, as if some children weren't told to keep their dirty hands off the walls. Dusty 'atta boy certificates are clustered above the fingerprints, too distant for me to read from where I sit without my glasses. I imagine they say what a great leader Sergeant Bluff is for turning weak boys into strong men.

"That's right." A Colgate smile stretches across Sergeant Bluff's face. "I saw you. You think I don't know what goes on with my soldiers? I know everything that goes on in my platoon. There's nothing that happens on this base that I don't know about. I know everything you do, everywhere you go. I see you. And I saw you walking with him."

"Oh, but Sergeant Bluff," Sergeant Samuels's says, his voice rising a couple of octaves, "that was before she got that car."

"Oh, yeah, that's right." Sergeant Bluff sprawls his legs out as he leans back in his chair. "You just got here, and you already got a car."

"I'm glad you got yourself a car, Burton." Sergeant Samuels's voice makes my teeth ache. "You said you liked my car that day I picked you up. And now you've gone and got yourself a real *nice* car. What kind is that you've got, Burton?"

"I don't know, Sergeant." I take a breath and hold it. Then I exhale, "It's a BMW. It's a 1985."

"Well," Sergeant Bluff raises his voice, "it's better than what I have. How about you, Sergeant Samuels, is that better than what you're driving?"

"Oh, it sure is, Sergeant Bluff."

Pain shoots up into my temples.

"I'm a sergeant and I can't even afford a car like that." Sergeant Bluff inches his face toward mine. "What makes you think you deserve a car like that when you're just a Specialist?"

It's as if a walnut has lodged into my throat. I can't breathe or swallow. Blood pulses behind my eyes. Sergeant Bluff takes notes of my trembling hands, so I stretch them out on my thighs, steadying them.

Sergeant Bluff smirks at me as if he knows he is eroding away my stoic façade. I take another breath, then exhale slowly. I regain my military bearing and sit in silence. He has no right to demand an answer about my private business as long as it doesn't interfere with my ability to soldier.

"We've been watching you since you got here," Sergeant Bluff says after a long pause. "We've been watching everything you do, everywhere you go. We see how you conduct yourself. You're a Specialist, but you're not conducting yourself like a Specialist."

As warm, angry tears sting my eyes, I am caught off-guard. I blink hard and swallow. "What do you mean, Sergeant?"

"We're just trying to help you, Burton," Sergeant Samuels

says, his voice soft. "We want you to succeed. We want to see you get ahead."

"You don't act like someone who wants to get ahead." Sergeant Bluff's brown eyes burrow into me. "We have certain ways of doing things in this company. If you don't want to move up, then we'll move you back down to Private."

"I don't understand what you are talking about. Why would I be demoted? Have I done something wrong, Sergeant?"

"Think about it for a minute, Burton. We think you know."

I stare up at the ceiling to contemplate what I have done wrong. In the Army there is no such thing as an innocent soldier. We may have forgotten to clean up our work stations, or plug in a forklift, or clean a latrine. The punishment could be severe, even if the infraction is small, so I am hesitant to confess to anything.

"I don't know, Sergeant." I shake my head and shrug my shoulders. "I just can't think of anything."

"C'mon, Burton." Sergeant Bluff raises his voice. "Stop playing games. You know exactly what we're talking about."

I slink down in my chair and stare at the floor. The only big thing that comes to mind is my recent poor performance at the rifle range. I failed to hit the minimum number of targets that first day and had to go back the next day. The last time I shot an M-16 was at pop-up targets at Basic in 1997, two and a half years ago. It was snowing, I couldn't stop shivering, and I had never shot at paper targets. The rifle they issued me had crooked sights. Part of me wondered if they gave me an abused rifle on purpose to test me. A soldier always finds a work-around, she never makes excuses, she adapts and overcomes, and succeeds in the face of failure. I failed, though. Sergeant Bluff refused to speak to me the rest of the day.

"Is it my boots, Sergeant?" I sit up in my chair and offer up the go-to problem drill sergeants complained about in Basic. I still refuse to incriminate myself. I look back and forth between

Sergeant Bluff and Sergeant Samuels. "Are they not shiny enough? Or is it my uniforms? Do they need more starch?"

Their eyes widen as they look at one another. They say nothing and I sink back into my seat. My heart thumps up into my throat as a lightbulb goes off in my brain. I think I finally get it. They still want something more, something bigger.

"Is it my run, Sergeants? I know I fall back in formation on the morning runs." I look down at my lap, trying to seem repentant, then up at the sergeants as I offer a solution to a made-up problem. "But I can pass my PT test. I haven't even been given a PT test since I got here, but I am sure I can pass it, Sergeants."

The two Non-Commissioned Officers talk to one another using a silent body language. The NCO's eyes widen, then narrow. They take deep breaths, then exhale. They raise their eyebrows, roll their eyes. Sergeant Samuels tilts his head to his right. Sergeant Bluff keeps his gaze fixed straight ahead.

I try to interpret what they are saying and I think I know. I smile. They are tired. I bet they are ready to take a bow and exit stage left.

"Burton!" Sergeant Bluff screams into the side of my face. The labyrinth of my inner ear vibrates, and I feel knocked off-balance. "I'm going to ask you again. Do you want to move up or do you want to move down? I can make it happen either way."

Sergeant Samuels moves to my right and crosses his arms. I look up at the two men hovering over me. The room spins around me until I no longer know where I am. "I don't understand, Sergeant." I drop my head to regain my equilibrium.

"You have the things you have because of me," Sergeant Bluff's voice grows deeper and slower. "Everything you have is because I allow it."

My cheek stings and eyes water as if someone slapped me.

"You want to act like a Private, then I'm going to start treating you like a Private," Sergeant Bluff says. Sergeant Samuels snorts.

"You will have nothing. That big room you have... That's not for Privates."

I wipe at my eyes, my nose.

"That car you have out there... Privates don't drive cars like that. You won't be able to afford to keep it when I bust you down a few ranks."

"And that little boyfriend of yours... What are you going to do, Burton, when he breaks up with you because he never sees you? You'll be out in the field, going to every FTX, every mission we support. I'll put you on every extra duty we have, you'll work evenings, weekends, holidays. Privates get the shittiest duties. Do you know that, Burton?"

I stare up at Sergeant Bluff and he meets my eyes.

"Listen, Burton," Sergeant Samuels says, assuming a good cop voice. "Don't you want to get out of the back of the warehouse? Don't you want to work up front with the other females, with Specialist Lemske and Specialist Peterson?"

"Yes, I guess, Sergeant. I mean, I want to learn my MOS. I want to learn the entire warehouse."

"You'll be working in the back of the warehouse with guys like Low and Dale for the rest of your life," Sergeant Bluff says. "If you want to work up front then you, you need to show us a little more respect. You need to be a team player like the rest of your fellow soldiers."

"I don't understand what you mean by team player, Sergeant." My mouth draws tight, I gulp down tears.

"Stop playing dumb, Burton. I think you know what we're talking about. I think you know what you need to do."

The seat whines as I straighten up. I squint at the tiny desk clock sitting on top of a bookshelf containing military manuals. I can't see the time. I look at the photo calendar still turned to last month on the opposite wall. January's picture is a tank with its huge gun erect, pointing into the air. I look back up at the ceiling;

watermarks the color of piss stain the drop tile. The tile is familiar. It is identical to the one in my father's house in Cincinnati where, when I was six or seven years old, my younger brother and I visited him every other weekend.

The weekends followed a script. On Friday afternoon my father showered my brother Jonas and me with hugs and kisses until we fell asleep late that night. Saturday was mandatory fun day, when he took us shopping for new clothes, toys, books, and movies. Early Sunday, Jonas and I sat on the oversized scratchy floral couch, dressed in our spiffy new outfits our father specifically chose for us so we could show Mom what a great dad he was. Jonas played with his new Hot Wheels cars and I thumbed through a picture book of Disney's Alice in Wonderland. But something in my father's demeanor always changed on Sunday. He always saw something in me that enraged him.

He ordered me to put down my book, stand up, and come with him. I followed him to the kitchen where he pulled out a chair and motioned for me to sit. He stood over me and scowled. I trembled and asked what I had done wrong. He said I was stupid, but not that stupid. I scrunched up my face. I tasted salty tears. He told me when I cried I was just as ugly and pathetic as my "whore of a mother". I told him I was sorry, and I didn't know what I did wrong. He said I had ruined the entire weekend. I didn't know how to behave properly, and I needed to be more like my brother.

Unlike Jonas, he said, I failed to show how much I loved my father and appreciated everything he gave me. I only had the toys, the beautiful clothes, the books because he let me, because he loved me and thought I loved him back. But he had made a mistake. When he was finished with me, I was to pack up everything in a box and hand it over.

"Then can I please go now?" I asked.

He said I was a big girl, and if I wanted to leave, if I wanted to keep my things I knew what to say, what to do.

Slumping into silence, I studied the calendar by the fridge with our visitation weekends circled in red ink. Today was the last day. I watched the second hand of the kitchen wall clock, encouraging the minute and hour hands to come along as it made its journey around the numbers. Only five, now four more hours until legally he had to return me home. I zoned out, stared up at the drop-tile ceiling.

I couldn't do it. I wouldn't give him what he wanted. I refused to say, "Daddy, I love you."

I pick at the cracks in the skin of my left index finger. Black warehouse dust mixes with blood. "I don't know what to do, Sergeant."

"Then why don't you talk to the females up front. Ask them what it means to be a team player." Sergeant Bluff lowers his voice. "Why don't you just ask Lemske and Peterson what they did to get to where they are? But we think you already know."

"No, Sergeant. I don't know." I look up. "Please just tell me what to do."

They say nothing.

Tears blur my vision. I look toward the door. "Please, Sergeants," I say, in a childlike voice that surprises me. "Please, can I go?" I look down at the floor between my boots, hoping whoever is in charge will at last call, "Cut", but no one intervenes. Tears break through the dam, I drop my head and sob.

Sergeant Bluff and Sergeant Samuels exchange glances. Unspoken words hang in the air.

At last Sergeant bluff yells at my head, still dropped to my chest, "Get up, you're dismissed."

Sergeant Samuels turns his back. I stand up and rush to the door.

"Burton," Sergeant Bluff calls after me. I turn around, but I am too ashamed to look at him. I have failed, but I don't know how.

"Don't let anyone see you looking like that. Go next door to the latrine and wash your face," Sergeant Bluff says. "And don't talk about this with anyone."

"Yes, Sergeant."

Next door, in the POL platoon's building, I slam the door to the latrine and lock it behind me. I turn on the faucet and pick up the sliver of ivory soap streaked black from countless filthy hands fondling it. I squeeze the bar of soap until it flops into the sink.

I slide down the wall onto the floor and put my head between my knees. The water drowns my cries.

After a few minutes I wipe my face. I stand and walk to the sink where I wash my dirty, tear-stained face. In the mirror I rehearse my lines and facial expressions until they seem natural. "Yes, Sergeant. No, Sergeant. Hey, Dale. Hey, Low. Y'all want to go to chow today?" I practice my lines over and over until I am ready to go back onstage.

Chapter 6

Interesting People

After my brother joined the Army he slapped a bumper sticker on his car that said, "Join the Army, Travel the World, Meet Interesting People, and Kill Them." He slapped it right next to his U.S. Army Infantry Sticker. Mom told him it didn't mean what he thought it did. He shrugged. I didn't know what she was talking about either. He said he was going to scratch out kill and write fuck, since Army guys get laid by hot, interesting, foreign chicks all over the world.

I haven't killed anyone. Yet. And hot, interesting, foreign guys aren't lining up to sleep with female soldiers. I traveled across the world, and all I've seen is a lot of the inside of a warehouse, a lot more of the inside of a latrine. I've seen a lot of the range, picking up spent brass after some company fired their M-16s or their Squad Automatic Weapon machine guns. I've seen a lot of this base, picking up other people's empty pop bottles and discarded Marlboro Lights. Sergeant Bluff has made good on his promise during our meeting in his office to put me on every shit duty he can find.

By Final Formation on Friday I can taste the weekend. It tastes like vodka shots and hitting the *disko* with my buddies Low and Dale. The entire company is gathered upstairs in the converted attic of our HQ building, waiting for the First Sergeant. The unusually beautiful spring days earlier in the week have returned to the more typical cool, rainy climate I assume is typical of Bavaria in February. Instead of outside at the basketball court behind the barracks, this is where we're holding formation. Although I've never been here, the room feels familiar with its dingy greige walls and grimy windows that won't open. I have a feeling all attics in old German buildings must look like this.

"Low and I are going to see how many chicks we can pick up this weekend." Dale elbows me. "We've decided it's time you get laid, so we're going to find you a hot German boyfriend at the *disko*." He grins a boyish smile at me. Since his blond buzzcut and cute dimples have been irresistible to local girls, perhaps he thinks he can work his charms on their brothers for me. I blush and look at Low who grins a wide, toothy grin at my embarrassment.

The final minutes until the weekend pass like hours. I hope the First Sergeant doesn't drag out his briefing about that ridiculous Easter Egg Hunt and Party no one except soldiers with families give a shit about. I'm ready to change out of my uniform and forget I'm a soldier for the next two days. I look around the room at a group of soldiers gathered near the wall.

"Where's your name, Burton?" someone asks. I turn to see Sergeant Samuels behind me. "I don't see your name on that list." He glances at his watch and sighs. "We need some more people to sign up for the party and you haven't volunteered yet."

"Oh, what list, Sergeant?" I ask. I stand at ease, trying hard not to fidget as I put my hands behind my back.

"The sign-up sheet for the Easter party. It's over there on the wall." He points to a paper taped to the dingy cinder block wall where the group of soldiers are gathered.

I make my way over to the paper. Scribbled beside each name I expect to find words like chocolate chip cookies, napkins, and soda. Instead, there are times and a host of duties involving cleanup, set-up, hiding eggs, and babysitting officers' kids. I study the sheet. Every name belongs to a female soldier in the company. There are only a few blank spaces left: time slots for babysitting.

At family and church gatherings when I was just a girl, husbands, fathers, and sons gathered in living rooms to discuss important business and to decide what was best for their families and communities. Women gathered with daughters and infant sons in kitchens to prepare meals. There would always be some lady who would try to shove a squalling child, not much younger than me, into my arms. I would refuse, hand the brat off to some willing woman, and run off to join my brother and cousins in throwing rocks at Papaw's old barn.

"There's something wrong with a girl who won't hold a baby," I heard my own kin say about me.

Putting pen to paper, I stop and look over my shoulder at Sergeant Samuels standing with Sergeant Bluff and some other high-ranking male sergeants, laughing. I turn toward the wall and press the pen harder into the paper, but I can't write my name. I walk away and join Low and Dale who are undoubtedly conspiring about the weekend.

"Burton," Sergeant Samuels calls my name again. "Come over here. Did you sign up?"

"No, Sergeant." My voice shakes.

"Why not?" Sergeant Bluff jumps in.

"Everything's taken, Sergeant."

"It is?" Sergeant Samuels asks, surprised. "C'mon, let's go have a look. I'm sure not everything's taken."

"Well, not *everything*, Sergeant," I say. "There's just babysitting. And I can't babysit, Sergeant."

"Why not?" Sergeant Bluff asks.

I want to ask him why. Why didn't he ask Low or Dale? Why do I have to watch kids that aren't mine? Why me? Why always me?

"Sergeants." I look back and forth between Sergeant Bluff and Sergeant Samuels. "Only the females have volunteered. If you need more soldiers to babysit, why don't you ask one of the males? None of them have volunteered."

Silence falls over the group of NCOs. Sergeant Bluff stares at me until I look at the floor, the wall, anything but his eyes piercing me.

"Just go sign up, Burton." Sergeant Samuels shakes his head and turns away as if to say this conversation is over.

"I can't babysit, Sergeant," I say. "Please don't make me volunteer, Sergeant."

The other sergeants shuffle their feet, grunt, and look away. Sergeant Bluff looks like he is about to speak, but glares at me, as if waiting for me to change my mind. I stare up at him and say nothing. He returns my silence. At last, I do an about face. I feel the two men's eyes on the back of my head as I walk away to rejoin my friends.

Chapter 7

Fall From Grace

On the third-floor hallway of the drafty company HQ building, I stand at the most ungodly hour in the morning in a queue along with the rest of my company. The dim amber glow of the exposed lightbulbs overhead flicker and threaten to blow. Inside my heather gray hoodie with ARMY written across the chest, I shiver and disappear. It was issued when I enlisted two and half years ago at the start of Basic. I lost almost thirty pounds from the time the size medium was issued to me at the start of training until I graduated eight weeks later. Even after last year and all that Instant Ramen I ate in the freshman dorm at Eastern Kentucky University, after all that beer I drank during Annual Training in Alabama with the Reserves, this thing still hangs loose.

Part of me wishes I could go back. I wish I could return to when I was fresh out of training, a Reservist, and still in high school. I was so proud to be a soldier that I couldn't resist wearing the ARMY hoodie a couple of times with jeans to class. Even Mom couldn't help taking out an ad in the local paper proclaiming her daughter had graduated Basic Training. For the first time, I knew I was worth something. My family, my community, hell, my country loved me.

On this morning in late February the walls of the company HQ building reek of damp, slimy mildew. I do not know how old this building is. In my imagination it was once a tower used during the dark ages for countless punishments, imprisonments, and tortures. At the end of the hallway, outside a filmy window, peeks a midnight blue sky. If and when the sun rises, it will be of no concern to me. I have been sentenced to the dark hole in the back of the warehouse where I'll spend all day unless Sergeant Bluff taps me for another trash police call or range detail.

My fellow soldiers take turns stepping onto the two physician's scales pulled out of storage just for this event—the company weigh-in. Weights, body types, even behavior garner comments, cheers, and jeers as if we are boxing champs stepping onto the scales before a big fight.

First Sergeant Dean appears at the door of his office holding a stack of personnel files with the top folder open. He wears his hair in an authoritative high and tight. The sides are shorn close enough to show off the bumps of in-grown hairs. Army-issued fleece can't hide that he's bolted together like a World War II fighter plane.

Behind me someone says, "The First Sergeant is so squared away he even starches his PT uniform." Soldiers laugh and I think it must be hyperbole. But when I squint I can make out an actual crease in our leader's sweatpants.

"This company," he says, slapping a manila folder shut, "is a disappointment."

A stillness falls over the building. I chew my bottom lip.

"You're a disappointment to me, to your NCOs, and to the Army," he continues. I shake my head. "I don't know how most of you even pass your PT tests, I don't. A good percentage of you are overweight, you need to be taped. This is a disgrace."

The soldier behind me whispers, "We're fucked now."

Heat from a company's worth of soldiers collects around my head. The damp coolness from earlier gives way to a warm humidity. The bodies are closing in on me as they move forward to see First Sergeant Dean. I can't see over their shoulders. I smell the stench of our collective anxiety.

"You may be a bunch of Quartermasters," the First Sergeant shouts loud enough for me buried among the bodies to hear, "but that isn't an excuse for you to be fat and lazy. You're soldiers first. Your MOS is second. If this stack of files I just picked up is any indication of the entire company's weight and PT scores, then we're not even deployable. You're trained to fight and defend your country. Most of you can't even outrun the enemy, how are you going to fight?"

A few people laugh. Someone shouts, "Hooah, First Sergeant." My stomach is sour. It's the smell, the noise, the lights or maybe the hunger. I look at my watch and wonder if there will be a line at the chow hall for breakfast by the time we're done. I want to go grab a croissan'wich from Burger King, but since this morning I have sworn off fast food. I could skip breakfast. I could run faster, do more sit-ups and push-ups if I didn't eat that junk, the Army says. The scale reads one-ten. But if I lost a few pounds, replaced that fat on my belly with cut abs by the next weigh-in, my sergeants would see I was dedicated. Maybe then I would be good enough.

The First Sergeant lowers his voice. "Platoon Sergeants, I'm talking to you now." I stand on my tiptoes to see him hand off the pile of folders to a big, hulking NCO.

"This is on you. You need to get your soldiers in shape. I want to see improvements."

First Sergeant Dean walks back into the office and I lower myself off my toes. A loud, male voice from the front of the hallway interrupts the rumbling of voices moving over my head.

"Listen up," the voice who must belong to the POL platoon sergeant says. "You all heard the First Sergeant. You'd better get your lazy, fat asses downstairs for some PT."

The crowd grumbles and does an about-face, heading for the narrow door leading from the hallway to the stairwell. We haven't all been weighed-in, but it's over now.

"Y'all better get a move on," the man's voice bellows down the hall. "Y'all better double-time down those stairs. Move it soldiers, unless you want to make up PT after final formation this evening."

"Hooah, Sergeant," a bass voice descends onto my head.

"Double-time, double-time," another voice shouts as its owner makes his way closer to me and the door.

Two, maybe three soldiers at most can fit through the door at one time, but that doesn't stop as many as possible from trying to shove their way through. The closer I get to the stairwell, the farther away it seems. I'm met with elbows, shoulders, and what feels like a knee to my lower ribs as I try to funnel my way through the doorway. I elbow someone's ribs.

"Aww, goddammit, you almost knocked out my tooth," a squeaky-voiced woman to my left calls out. "You're all insane. You're just slowing things down. Formation can't start until most of us get down there, anyway. This is ridiculous."

She may or may not be the soldier I hit, but I stop throwing elbows. She's right, this is ridiculous. I proved my point, if only to myself, I can hold my own. I fall back. The others pass me and stampede for the door.

In the stairwell, I hesitate. Looking down the three flights of steps, I shake. It's darker than I remember when I came up this morning. I look down at the narrow, twisting stairs. The stone they're carved from looks like it could have moss growing in the cracks. The chewed and broken steps are narrow, designed when men's feet were not much bigger than my size three combat boots.

There's little to no lighting. I don't know if someone forgot to turn the lights on this morning or if back in the day these sorts of buildings didn't have stairwell lighting. Soldiers run past me down the stairs. I shake my head. I say to no one, "I can't see a thing. I'm not running down those."

I fall in behind a single file of soldiers walking down the right side of the stairs. While they keep their shoulders hugging the wall, a steady stream of our comrades rushes past them to their left, like cars in the fast lane of the *Autobahn*. It seems like a sure and safe bet to get down the three flights of gnarly stairs until we're hit with a wave of soldiers from behind. It's like a dam breaking, and I hear the impending doom before I feel it.

The roaring laughter and thunder of feet come up from behind me, and I move as close to the wall as possible. It doesn't matter, as there are too many soldiers and they crash into me from every direction. I am shoved into the wall, then I fall forward into the guy in front of me. My foot twists, and I slip on one of the slippery stairs. I fall backwards into someone behind me, then I'm somehow pushed back upright, landing on my feet. My left ankle hurts, but I'm okay.

"Y'all need to stop running before you hurt someone," a male voice behind me calls out.

My heart pounds up into my throat. My brain works out in just a few milliseconds the thousands of catastrophes I just avoided. I could have really been hurt. I could have hit my head and got a concussion because our NCOs ordered us to run down some stairs so they could show off for the First Sergeant. I could have twisted my ankle and ended up with a career-ending injury just because some soldiers wanted to look gung-ho. Everything I worked for would be gone.

Then I wonder if that would be so bad. If I got hurt, perhaps my company would get rid of me. As a woman I don't seem to be worth much, but as an injured woman I would be worthless. Since they wouldn't want me, they might have let me transfer to the 316th where I was supposed to go. Maybe they would just kick me out. Sergeant Bluff has made it clear that he doesn't want me in his company or even in the Army.

It was just last week, I think, he stopped Dale, Low, and me, laughing as we walked back to our section, to let us know how much he thought of us.

"Do you know what?" Sergeant Bluff said. "You're all worthless. You're worthless to me, you're worthless to the Army, and you're worthless to your families back home."

Low's face was blank, but Dale's cheeks blushed as if he'd been slapped.

Stepping back to look at the three of us, he continued, "You join the Army, thinking you're going to be somebody, but you're nothing. You're not worth as much as that Deuce-and-a-Half sitting outside. The Army would be more upset if I came back from the field without a truck than if I came back without one of you."

Dale's Adam's apple bobbed up and down as he swallowed and stared at the floor. Low straightened his mouth and looked out from underneath his eyelids.

"You're cannon fodder." Sergeant Bluff stared at us. "You're here so some rich guys in suits sitting in fancy offices up in D.C. can move you around the world, like pawns on a chessboard. They send you to die in a jungle or they send you to an oil field. It's not about protecting democracy. It's about money for them. No one gives a shit about soldiers. No one will remember you. Not even your family."

His eyes focused on something somewhere distant. I wondered if he was remembering some desert or swamp to where he had once deployed. What he said couldn't be true, I thought. America is the good guy, defending democracy at home and around the world. We soldiers were the good guys, too, protecting

America's freedom. Yes, soldiers do what other people cannot or will not, I thought, but that is what makes us strong and brave. That is what I had always been taught. It could not be true that we were disposable to the country and its people. If he was right, why would a man of his rank stay in the Army and risk his life for another man's fortune?

"You're worth more dead than alive." He glared at each of us. "If you died right now, you would go home heroes. Your parents would be the proud parents of brave soldiers who sacrificed for their nation. They would be $250k richer thanks to that big insurance policy the Army offers worthless individuals like yourselves." He didn't pause for a breath or to even find his words. "That's all you're worth to anyone. If you had any value to anyone, you wouldn't be here. When the Army gets done with you and all you are is some broke-down useless veteran, see how happy they are to have you when they didn't want you before. The best thing you can do for you, your family, and your country is to go home in a box with a flag draped over it."

From my English 102 professor, Dr. Harris, I knew the nation pulled from its pool of poor and minority men for the draft during Vietnam. Rich men and their children were too important to be sacrificed. But I thought that ugly part of our country was behind us now. We volunteered to join. Granted, almost every soldier I knew was poor, looking for opportunity, or trying to escape their civilian lives. I wondered what Sergeant Bluff was escaping, what kept him year after year in an institution that was using him.

Sergeant Bluff's words haunt me this morning. If I were discharged early, I could not go home. I would have no money, nowhere to live. Mom told me a long time ago not to count on her for anything after I turned eighteen. I'm on my own. And she doesn't want to hear what I say when I call home. She told me to stop whining and pull my shit together and stop making myself into a target. If I go home, she will say I screwed up my life. She will tell me how I've given her nothing to be proud of and I'm an embarrassment. She loves me not because I am her daughter, but because I'm a soldier.

Sergeant Bluff was right about everything.

If I fell, and smashed in my brains or snapped my neck it would be better for everyone, even me. I could rest and be at peace. Every day of my life has felt like a fight to survive. After twenty years of living and fighting, I worry that is all I'll ever know. I don't know how I'll get through the next twenty years, or the next month, or even today. I am tired of fighting.

Behind me there's a rumble of footsteps. "Here comes another group," a soldier says, pulling my attention to the pounding above us. "We got to go."

Like some architectural heart, the doorway pumps out soldiers in regular increments. I take a deep breath and jump. I lunge forward into dark, empty space, feeling nothing under my feet until I land on the next step. I hear the roar of soldiers coming down the steps behind me, closing in on me. I am too cautious, feeling my way along the wall, groping with my feet for the stairs. I'm engulfed by the next wave of soldiers. I worry I might suffocate or drown in sweat. I feel nothing except men's bodies encapsulating me.

In the next moment I'm on my hands and knees with my left foot twisted behind my ass. The pain is instantaneous and searing. I can't speak, or even breathe. On all fours, I am paralyzed on the last landing of the staircase. Because I'm a soldier, I am not permitted to make noise or show pain. I fight the instinct to scream or cry from the hurt, humiliation, and guilt. Shockwaves of pain move through my left ankle and knee as I try to push myself up. My body betrays me, it revolts as I try to stand.

"What happened," a soldier on his way down the stairs asks.

I can only shake my head, as I struggle to figure out how I ended up on the floor.

"Someone shoved her," the tall guy who must have been behind me on the stairs says. "It was an accident, but I knew something like this would happen. These people in this company... I swear. I don't know why they do the things they do."

It's my fault, I did it to myself, I willed this into reality, I think. Even as I sicken of my own thoughts, the words still bubble up inside my head. I bite my lip and clamp my eyes shut to hold back tears. I think about how hard I've tried to take Mom's advice since I've been here, to think positive, so I'll bring positive energy. She always warned me, likewise, that my negative thoughts would create negativity. Even in my Psych class, my professor talked of how powerful the subconscious could be in creating what it wanted.

My mind rolls back the videotape of my fall. There was a herd of soldiers, I was running, someone slammed into me, it was so dark, I couldn't see, I missed that last step. I had an accident, which I wouldn't have had if the NCOs hadn't been negligent. I would have never wanted any of this to happen, my rational mind says. Fuck subconscious brains and negative energies, yet I still carry a small twinge of guilt.

"Ouch," another soldier says from a few steps up. I roll over to my left and onto my ass and cup my ankle. "I heard that crunch all the way up here." He looks like some rubbernecker who has come upon the scene of a fiery crash and it's the highlight of his day.

The tall guy asks, "Can you stand up?"

I shake my head. "I tried. I can't get up."

I don't know anyone's names because I'm so new. Since we don't wear our ranks on our PT uniforms, I don't even know if I should address them as Sergeant. I can barely make out anyone's features. My world is black and white and out of focus. I don't know if it's because the staircase is so dark or if I'm blinded by pain.

"C'mon." A black hand reaches toward my face. "I'll help you up. Can you put weight on your foot?"

I grab the man's hand and he pulls me onto my right foot. I tap my left toes to the ground. Electricity shoots through the fillings in my back teeth. "I can't," I say. "It hurts too much." I pull my left foot up and buckle at the right knee.

The other soldier stands by, directing traffic around me.

"Stand up, don't sit back down. Just give it a few minutes," the soldier holding my hand says. "If you can put weight on it and take more than two steps, it's not broken. You won't have to go to sick-call unless it's broken."

"Yeah," the second guy says. "No need to go to sick-call when all they'll give you is some Motrin. And we all know you don't want to go to sick-call in the Army unless you're dying."

"Especially in this company," my good Samaritan says. "They just think you're trying to get out of PT or going to the field. You could have a bone sticking out of your leg and they'd say you were faking just to get out of some duty. You definitely don't want to go to sick-call unless you have to."

My pain and embarrassment give way to anxiety. I touch my toes back down to the ground and hold my breath. I ease my heel down and try to ignore the sharp pain coming from my ankle. If I put most of my weight on my right leg and walk on my left toes, I can hide my injury.

"I'm okay." I nod at the soldier. "I can walk. You can let go now. I'm good. Thank you."

He looks down at my left foot. "Are you sure?"

"Yes, I'm sure," I smile. "I mean it still hurts a little, but I'll be fine."

"Okay."

I wait while he and his buddy make their way down the stairs, then I grab the handrail and hobble down the last flight.

I'm the last soldier outside. The sky has turned a pretty pale blue, and the sun is burning away the clouds. Loose platoon formations are forming in lieu of the more formal company PT formations. Soldiers unzip their ARMY hoodies. Some hard-ass sergeant is hot, so he must have ordered all of us to strip down to our t-shirts. The cool air stings my warm, sweaty arms as I take off my sweatshirt.

"There you are, Burton," Sergeant Samuels calls to me. Our platoon has gathered on the cobblestone street just outside the front doors of the Company HQ building. "We knew we were missing someone."

I make my way towards the group as fast as I can, hoping no one notices my limp.

"PT's going to be fast today," he announces to the platoon. "Sergeant Bluff left me in charge since he had some stuff up at the SSA to take care of. We don't have a lot of time because we have to get up there, so we're going to knock out some sprints, show the First Sergeant we're motivated, dedicated. Hooah?"

Sergeant Samuels grins his toothy smile and motions for us to divide into two groups facing one another.

"I love sprints, Sergeant," Peterson smiles. "I used to run track in high school. My mom still has all my trophies in my room back home." Her ability to keep pace with the fastest men in the company combined with her muscular calves make me believe she is telling the truth. I wonder why my calves never bulked up from all the running and playing in the mountains I did as a kid.

The other soldiers shout, "Hooah," like he just offered to buy us all ice cream for dinner.

"Sergeant Samuels would be a good platoon sergeant if it wasn't for Sergeant Bluff," Dale leans in and whispers to me.

"Yeah," I say, "he's just the best fucking guy in the world."

"You know, Burton," Dale steps back, "you've got a negative attitude sometimes. You could do a lot better in the Army if you just had a better outlook."

"Fuck you, Dale. We're friends, but don't lecture me on the Army."

Dale curls his upper lip into a snarl. My concern right now is not with our strained friendship. My ankle threatens to crack and give way under my weight. I practice standing without crying as I wait for my turn to run. It's impossible. I need to find the right moment, pull Sergeant Samuels to the side, and tell him what happened.

Specialist McKenzie, just back from maternity leave, catches her breath after her first turn. "Fuck, this hurts. They don't make nursing bras for sprinting."

Specialist Ford runs toward our side, howling, with her arms crossed across her flopping breasts. "Oh, my God, my tits. The PX carries such shitty sports bras..."

"Sergeant," McKenzie says, "How many of these sprints do we have to do?"

"A few more." Sergeant Samuels looks at his watch and gives the two women a sad look. "Just do the best you can."

"Females," Horne says, rolling his eyes at Sergeant Samuels.

I want to hit Horne. I have never liked him, not even when we were together in the same class at AIT in Ft. Lee. A few of the women soldiers "fed up with his and his buddies sexist behavior" reported them to the drill sergeants. Horne and the others threatened to bust past the fireguards on our all-female floor and throw us a sock party while we slept. I shuttered to think what else they might do, but we all kept vigilant fireguard over the next week, until our male comrades seemed to forget the incident.

I never forgot it. And I will never forgive the universe for its sick cosmic joke when it threw Horne and I have back together here in Germany.

Sergeant Samuels smiles, as if to be polite, but says nothing.

Maybe Dale is right, without Sergeant Bluff around Sergeant Samuels might not be such a dick and have a little empathy. I think about revealing my injury and asking if I can go get it checked out at sick call.

"Your turn, Burton," Peterson says from the starting line. My ankle throbs when I put weight on it. I don't know how to push the piercing pain out of my mind to walk, let alone run.

"Yeah," Horne says. "You always fall out of the long company runs because you can't keep up. What's going to be your excuse for sprints? You can't say your tits bother you because you're flatter than me."

Sergeant Samuels, Sergeant Bennett, Peterson, and Lemske all chuckle.

Trying not to limp, I make my way to Sergeant Samuels by the starting point. There's no use in telling anyone I'm hurt. Before anyone has even seen me sprint once, they are convinced of my inability to do it and that I will try to make some excuse as to why. If I suck it up, just for a couple of sprints, if I do them fast, they will stop seeing me as a total failure.

Sergeant Samuels calls out, "OK Burton, on your mark... get set... and go."

In a flash I'm kicking my heels up to my rear. I'm to the other side before the pain has time to register.

"Wow, Burton," Sergeant Samuels sounds surprised. "Sprinting might be your thing."

"Good job," Dale slaps me on the back, already forgiving our tiff.

Horne rolls his eyes. Peterson, Lemske, and Sergeant Bennett snicker. By the time I report to the warehouse in an hour or two, the one impossible hurdle I managed to clear will already have been forgotten, or at least repackaged to highlight my short-comings.

My ankle throbs. I can't touch my heel to the ground. The pain is unlike anything I've ever felt, and I'm sure it must be broken. I long to crawl off alone behind a bush to lick my wounds.

On the ground my hoodie is marked with a shoe print. I pick it up, dust it off. Holding it to my flat chest, I can still smell home. It smells like my closet where it hung next to my Green Day and Nirvana t-shirts. It smells like Mom's Tide powders when I washed it after my last Reserves Drill. This afternoon I will do laundry with my off-brand PX liquid detergent and wash all that away.

CHAPTER 8

ONE MORE DAY

Every evening after work for the last month I have wondered how I will make it through one more day. Despite my best efforts to tell myself I'm fine, my left ankle I twisted a few days ago tells me otherwise. It tells me I'm hurt, unwell. Sickly is how Mamaw would've described it. I hate that word. I always did, but there is no doubt this word describes my foot. With its sallow and puffy skin and the ugly blue, black, and green bruise, it makes me ill to see it.

To hide the evidence during the day, I lace my boots as tight as they will go. I furrow my brow and set my jaw against the pain. I imagine I look hard, like a real soldier. In the evening, alone on my bed, I undo the laces and extract my swollen foot from the boot. Where no one can hear me, I allow a whimper. I fight nausea and tears. I give in to sobs, I give up. I call Mom.

"Hello," she answers in a cheerful voice. She knows it's me. I always call her at 1:00 pm her time, 1900 hours my time in Germany. She is home this time every day for her lunch break from her job as a home health nurse. I can talk to her, maybe. The man she married my senior year of high school, who I can't bring myself to call my stepfather, doesn't like me calling home. She told me he said I was twenty years old, too old to be calling my mommy from the Army in Germany. He's not there in the afternoons, so he can't tell Mom to hang up.

"Mom," I sniffle into the receiver. "I can't take it. I don't know what to do."

"What's wrong," she asks. I hear the worry in her voice. "What's happened?"

I want to tell her everything, but I don't know where to begin. I want to say how hard it is, so much harder than Basic or AIT, that I'm so lonely, even that I miss her and Kentucky, just a little. I want to say I wish someone would hold me. I wish I could tell her how I didn't know the Army was going to be like this because it was never like this before. I want to say that I just wanted to do something good with my life, to make her proud, and to have a shot at a better life, but I have fucked up. I don't know what I did wrong, but I made a mistake.

I can't say any of that. She would tell me she was right, that she knew I shouldn't go to the Army or Germany, that I wasn't tough enough. It is too late now, no use in crying about it, she would say. She would tell me to grow up and be a big girl and that being a grown-up means owning up to your mistakes and living with the consequences.

"It's my ankle." I regain my composure. "I hurt it pretty bad when I fell down some stairs the other day. The pain... I can't take it anymore."

"Is it broken?" she asks, flying into nurse-mode. "Are you putting ice on it and staying off of it? Did you get it x-rayed? What did the doctor say?"

I tell her I can't go to the doctor, that I'll be called a faker, a liar, someone who just doesn't want to work.

"That's ridiculous," she says. "If it's swollen, they'll know you're hurt."

"It doesn't work like that in the Army," I explain again, trying not to sob into the phone.

"I don't know what to do. I don't know how to do this."

A loud bang at my door sends me into a conspiratorial whisper. "Someone's here."

"Who?" she asks. "Who's there?"

"I don't know." I swallow a knot in my throat. "I don't want to see anyone. I don't want anyone to see me like this. I'm afraid..."

"Afraid of what?" she asks. "It's your Army. They're your people. You can trust them. Just answer it."

The phone connection crackles. In the background I make out the faint sounds of Mom's favorite daytime soaps. I picture her sitting on the couch in the living room in her royal blue nursing scrubs, wearing her reading glasses, with a pile of patients' files in her lap. Beside her she probably has a sandwich and glass of water as she cradles the phone between her shoulder and ear. I've seen her in this exact position, charting, watching TV, and eating, a hundred times. It always amazed me how effortlessly her pen glided over her paperwork or how professional she sounded when she called a doctor about a patient. She was never tired or frazzled or lost her temper until she took off her uniform at the end of the day.

"I figured you'd have a hard time keeping your mouth shut for long if someone ever said something to you." She pauses. "I'm not going to say I told you so, but..."

I can't tell her about the things I'd like to say. I can't tell her I don't really get to take off my uniform at the end of the day. I can't tell her that I don't have a say over what happens to me. I can't tell her I don't ever get to decompress, destress. She's my mom. She doesn't listen. I'm a soldier. I don't talk.

There is another knock at my door.

"I have to go," I say.

"Well, call me back later. I'm sure it's nothing. Probably just your friends. You always assume the worst, you know. You've always been so dramatic about everything. And I'm sure if you just talk to your sergeants or whoever it will be fine."

"Whatever. I can't call you later," I say. "It'll be almost midnight here by the time you get home and that husband of yours will be there. Look, I got to go see who's at the door."

"All right," Mom's voice drifts off. She is probably getting wrapped up in *All My Children* or *Days of Our Lives* right about now or writing about a difficult patient she just saw. "You get some rest. Go get an x-ray. Call me tomorrow then."

It isn't Dale or Low. I know their knocks, playful and irregular. This is the formal, insistent, and confident knock of a leader. I've already taken off my boots for the day, but I haven't gotten around to taking off the rest of my uniform. I always feel the need to be ready in case something happens. If I had to, I could stuff my sausage feet back into my wool socks stiff with the day's sweat and put my boots on. Walking over to the door in my fatigues and a pair of pink Adidas slider sandals, I open the door to find Sergeant Eldridge standing, tall and lanky, in the hallway, looking down at a piece of paper he's holding in his left hand.

"Hey, Burton." He barely glances at me. He raises the paper up to inspect it. "I didn't think you were in. Sergeant Bluff wanted me to come by this evening and talk to you, but I was just about to slide this under your door."

My heart falls into my stomach. "What is it, Sergeant?" I stare at the paper, trying to read the print through the backside of the paper. I worry I am in trouble, but for what I don't know. A soldier always worries they have done something wrong they aren't even aware of.

"I need to inspect your TA-50," he says. "Sergeant Bluff wants me to make sure you are issued all your gear before we head out to the field again."

"Yes, Sergeant." Relief rushes over me. One crisis averted.

Now I just have to avoid looking at him for fear he might see my bloodshot eyes. A soldier should never cry, or at least be seen crying. My voice gives me away.

"Are you okay?" Sergeant Eldridge cranes his neck down and looks at me for the first time. "Burton, what's wrong. Are you crying because you're homesick? It's okay. A lot of soldiers, it's their first time from home, they're in a new country..."

"I'm not homesick, Sergeant," I cut him off. "It's not that."

"Can I come in?" he asks as he closes the door behind him. "What's wrong, then? Is it Lemske and Peterson? I saw something went down between y'all today and I think they might have been kind of rough on you since you got here, but you have other friends, right? You and Dale and Low are buddies, right?"

"No, Sergeant, that's not it either." I took in a deep breath and looked up at the ceiling. I could never mention to my squad leader I was having difficulty with my fellow soldiers or issues adjusting to life in the Army. It would be admitting I had a problem, that I was the problem. "I mean, that stuff's fine. I have friends and I can deal with Lemske and Peterson, Sergeant."

"Okay, then. You can deal with them." He raises an eyebrow. "Then what's the matter? I'm your squad leader. I'm supposed to take care of my soldiers. I can't help you if you don't tell me."

I study his face, debating if I should trust him with the information. Dale told me the other day, "Don't trust anyone ranked Sergeant, E-5, and above. Our squad leaders only look out for themselves, they don't care about doing anything to help their soldiers. And the platoon leaders in this company use anything they can get against you. Don't talk to no one, if you can help it, but if you do, only talk to one of your buddies the same rank as you, like me or Low."

Sergeant Eldridge shrugs. "C'mon, Burton."

"It's my ankle, Sergeant," I blurt out, tears welling up. "Look at it. It's killing me. I can barely walk." It feels so good to admit it. It's like a dirty secret I've been dying to confess.

"Oh, my God." He stares down at my fat foot. "What happened?"

I explain about falling down the stairs after the weigh-in. I tell him how I'd run sprints that day, then a few miles the next, but it was today's road march that has finally pushed me over the edge.

A cloud of worry rolls over his face.

"Why don't you go to sick-call?"

"You know why, Sergeant." I stare up at him and try not to burst into tears again. "If I get a no-run, jump, or march profile, Sergeant Bluff and everyone else will say I'm just faking to get out of duty."

"Burton." Sergeant Eldridge cocks his head at me. "Just fall out with sick-call formation and go to the clinic tomorrow. They'll probably x-ray it. It might be broken. You need to get it looked at. I know you're not faking. I can see that."

"Okay, Sergeant."

"But when you go, you can't tell them you were running down the stairs. You can't tell them that the whole company was running, or that someone told you to run. You understand?"

With a blank look on my face I stare up at my squad leader.

"We're not supposed to be running down the stairs. They told us to stop doing that. We'll get in trouble, all of us, all the way up to the top. And you know they say shit rolls downhill in the Army." He looks at me to let me know where I am on this shit hill. "Who did you hear give the orders to run down the stairs? Was it the First Sergeant? Was it Sergeant Bluff? It wasn't me, was it? I know it wasn't me."

"I don't know, Sergeant." I look down, avoiding my squad leader's gaze. Suddenly I feel a rush of guilt, as if I made the decision myself to rush down the stairs and invite disaster. "I just heard someone yell, I thought it was a sergeant. He said we'd better get our asses down the stairs and everyone started pushing and running. I don't know, Sergeant."

"Okay, then. You don't know who. It could have just been some loudmouth Specialist."

"I guess, Sergeant. But he sounded like a sergeant."

"It doesn't matter. You don't know who it was. And I don't recall hearing anyone say that. No one else will remember it either. When you go to sick-call, just tell them you fell going down some stairs. It's not a lie, and that's all they need to know."

"Okay, Sergeant." I wipe my eyes.

"Okay," he says. "I'm going to leave this inventory list with you and let you go over it yourself. Just get some rest tonight. Let me know if any of your gear is missing, all right? You need to take care of yourself. Remember, Burton, I'm here. I've got your back."

"Yes, Sergeant," I say in a hurry to get him out of my room. Waves of relief rush over me, but I still want to curl up and be alone in my pain until I go to sick-call in the morning.

———

Friday morning I do as Sergeant Eldridge says. At the clinic, instead of x-raying my ankle, a doctor tells me almost verbatim what the soldier in the stairwell told me. He says if I can take more than a few steps, my ankle is not broken and to take two Tylenol every six hours. I am given a light duty profile for three days, told to ice it, elevate it, use an Ace bandage, and wear tennis shoes instead of boots.

I am not too happy about wearing the soft shoes of shame. Seeing soldiers hop around on crutches wearing ugly white running shoes with the green ties hanging out of the legs of their BDU trousers inspires pity, laughter, even disgust from those of us fortunate enough to not be hurt. At least I wasn't given crutches, I think as I put on the issued black wool socks and my pair of black shell-toe Adidas. I tie up the ankles of my trousers with elastic boot bands so the green strings don't hang loose. In the mirror propped up against my wall by the door I think I don't look too pathetic. An officer might shake his head at me for being such a pussy-ass female once I get close enough to salute him, but from a distance my injury might be camouflaged enough to go unnoticed.

Up at the SSA I head straight to my section and get to work. The doctor's appointment has made me late, but I figure it best not to mention my tardiness to my comrades. No one seems to notice my earlier absence or even my choice of footwear. There is too much work to do to worry about what I'm wearing or where I was for the first half hour or so. I ask what needs to be done, and my coworkers tell me where help is needed. I'm here now and that seems to be all that matters.

An hour into my return I think, everything will be okay, my world did not end because I saw a doctor. Then a sudden change, an eerie quiet descends on the back of the warehouse. The stereo clicks off. My comrades duck their heads into boxes, increase their strides as they walk to a pallet, whisper their communications. Even the forklifts seem to operate at a lower decibel. I can feel him, but when I turn around from my workstation, only an empty space, a gust of wind is left in his place. I know he was there. I look for him and find him talking to another soldier by a forklift. "Yes, Sergeant," the guy says to Sergeant Bluff. "We're on it, Sergeant." It's a standard answer, but the one he wants to hear. Sergeant Bluff seems satisfied and moves on.

I turn around, directing my attention to my box. If I don't look up, he won't see me. I'm doing nothing wrong, I tell myself. There is no reason for him to single me out, but I don't want to give him a reason. I know he's seen me, he's coming back for me. I wish I had my forklift license like Low and Dale. I wish I could hide in plain sight. Low told me, "I get on a forklift and go outside to get the heavy stuff. Sergeant Bluff won't mess with me so much if I'm out there picking up the lumber and concertina wire on a forklift."

"Specialist Burton," Sergeant Bluff yells from behind me. The sound bounces off the wall in front of my face until I'm engulfed in my own name filtered through his deep, gravelly voice.

Despite my best efforts to control it, my startle reflex gets the best of me. My crime has been discovered. I look at my work area, trying to find the fault before he does so I can be prepared. I can't find any, but I throw everything I've been counting back into the box, anyway.

"Yes, Sergeant." I have the look of the guilty pretending to be innocent.

He looks over my shoulder to see my table. He looks at my hand, the box cutter I'm still holding, before I close it up and throw it on the table and remember to put my hands behind my back and stand at ease.

"What is on your feet," he says, glancing at my shoes then staring into my face. Out of the corner of my eye I notice my comrades stealing glances for the first time at my feet. "Why aren't you in boots?"

"Oh, I have a soft shoe profile, Sergeant." I smile like it's no big deal.

"You have a profile?" he asks. "Do you have it on you? Let me see it."

I dig into the right pocket of my trousers for the slip of paper the doctor gave me this morning. Sergeant Bluff furrows his brow as he studies my doctor's order. He shakes his head and I wonder if I misinterpreted the doctor's orders.

"You went to sick-call this morning." He looks back up at me, still holding the paper. "And you got a profile? How long you been in this company?"

My heart thumps in its chest cavity. My comrades glance out

of the corner of their eyes, trying to determine what crime I have committed.

"Where's your squad leader," Sergeant Bluff demands. "Get Sergeant Eldridge over here."

"Right here, Sergeant." Sergeant Eldridge appears out of the ether beside me.

"Let's all go outside and have a little talk." Sergeant Bluff gives no other explanation. Sergeant Eldridge looks at me as if to ask if I fucked up. My eyes water and my face stings with the humiliation of a child who knows she is about to get it. Sergeant Bluff's words remind me of those same ones my teachers used when they took me out in the hallway to scold me or what Mom said when she took me outside the church and got a switch.

Outside of the warehouse I stand silent beside Sergeant Eldridge as Sergeant Bluff looks at us both without speaking. I pull my BDU cap down far over my forehead and look straight on with my hands locked behind my back.

"Did you know about this, Sergeant Eldridge?" Sergeant Bluff waves the evidence in front of my sergeant's face. "Did you know she went to sick-call and got a profile this morning?"

Sergeant Eldridge reaches out and takes it. "No, Sergeant," he says. "I had no idea."

My head snaps to look at Sergeant Eldridge to my left. He holds the paper out from his body, like reading the words sprained ankle or soft shoe profile are contagions. He hands the paper back to Sergeant Bluff.

"Did someone get to you, Burton?" Sergeant Bluff asks. "Tell you that if you went to sick-call and got a profile you'd get out of taking a PT test?"

I wait for Sergeant Eldridge to speak up, do the honorable thing, and admit the truth. I wait for him to step up, be the sergeant who last night had seen my injured foot, to be the leader who promised to have his soldier's back if she went to sick-call. He looks straight ahead as if I'm not even present. He sighs out a long breath, closes his eyes, and shakes his head as if he's stunned, ashamed of me.

"You're afraid you'll fail the PT test," Sergeant Bluff says, "and you're always falling out of the runs, so you thought you'd go get a profile."

He holds the small rectangular slip of paper up in front of me, gesturing for me to take it back. I stare at the creases and smudgy fingerprints. Already it looks soft and worn, as if I've been issued it days ago instead of just hours ago. It has a tear at the top along one of the folds. I reach out and take the paper, folding it in half. I think how easy it would be to rip it up like I once did in Basic. I hid a profile I'd gotten for heat exhaustion after puking my guts up on a sergeant's boots on a road march. My drill sergeant smiled as I ripped it up and put the pieces in my BDU pocket after he asked me about it. I said, "It doesn't say anything, Drill Sergeant." Maybe I looked gung-ho, maybe he was just overworked with too many recruits and didn't give a shit as long as I didn't die.

It's too late for any of that now. Sergeant Bluff for whatever reason has a vested interest in me. Right now I look anything but gung-ho, standing here in front of him, my old-school Adidas on my feet and a "light duty x 3 days" profile slip in my hand. Right now Sergeant Bluff is doing anything but smiling at me.

"I'm not afraid of a PT test." I stare out from under the bill of my cap at Sergeant Bluff. "I really did hurt my ankle. But I can pass the test. Any time you want to give it to me. I've been here two months. I've been waiting. I told you that in your office that day."

Sergeant Bluff moves closer to me, his eyes widen, and I wonder if he's going to stick the bill of his cap next to mine like drill sergeants do with their Smokey the Bear hats.

"It's 'Sergeant', Burton," Sergeant Eldridge turns to me. "Say

'Sergeant' when you address an NCO. Remember your military bearing."

"Right, Sergeant," I say to Sergeant Eldridge. I look at Sergeant Bluff. "Sergeant."

"Hmm-mmm, all right." He stares back at me. "We'll see about that. Your profile is for three days. The Army says I have to give you twice that time for recovery before I can test you. But be ready because as soon as you're off recovery, you're getting a PT test. I'm marking it on my calendar in the office."

Sergeant Bluff turns towards the front doors of the warehouse. Sergeant Eldridge trails behind him. I walk off in the opposite direction, towards the rear doors in shipping and receiving.

The warehouse is still. No one looks up, no one talks, not even the forklifts hum. Sergeant Bluff has spooked everyone and they've run like cockroaches when the lights come on. I smack my cap against my hand and look around for some work.

I pull up a chair at the desk with the stack of packing slips next to the computer. Looking up at the clock, I count the hours until chow. I add the minutes left on my morning, I subtract the time I get for lunch, then add in the afternoon hours of work, and calculate. It's only five and a half, maybe six more hours until the weekend. I'll rest all weekend. I'll be back in boots and running by Monday morning.

I flip the pages of the large calendar on the desk to the following week. It's a new month, March. I shouldn't have a problem passing a PT test by next month. Turning the pages further to November, to my twenty-first birthday, I wonder who I will be then. I will have been in this place for almost a year. In the few months since my arrival here, I am so changed from that Army Reservist who left Kentucky. That girl, that person I once was, no longer exists. The pages drop from my hand and the calendar returns to this month, this day. I stare back up at the clock on the wall.

CHAPTER 9

ONE TIRE AT A TIME

The smell of new rubber is a bold contrast to the musty, stale air of warehouses to which I've become accustomed over the last couple months here in Germany. The odor bypasses my nose and goes straight to my brain. It takes me back to another time, to old country garages and junkyards I visited as a little girl with Mom and Papaw back home in Knox County, Kentucky. Someone's kin or a friend of a friend was sure to have a brand-new used tire that would fit Mom's little black '83 Chevette. One tire at a time, sweet Jesus, is all we could afford until Mom could pick up an extra nursing shift at the hospital or my father started paying the child support he owed. Papaw said the Lord would provide, not to worry. "I can't wait around on the Lord," Mom would tell her dad. "The Lord helps those who help themselves, remember?" Then she would walk off in a huff, call her boss, call her lawyer.

This morning, the odor of something familiar yet different from what I've grown used to in the last few months brings me out of where I was and back to somewhere else. I look up and around for the source of my memory. Random parts—hoses, belts, nuts, bolts, even the gears and guts—of Army vehicles are scattered about my new world, 316th Maintenance Company's SSA Warehouse.

Behind me I hear the piercing noise of a wooden pallet slapping on concrete. I turn my head. My ears and eyes zero in on what my nose cannot. In the back of the bay I see the hulking, nubby tire banded down, too big for the broken pallet on which it sits. It resembles some wild animal, a gorilla perhaps, taken from the wild, strapped down, restrained and held captive. No doubt it is just passing through, held here in purgatory for an undetermined amount of time until some mech or motor sergeant picks it up and takes it to its final home.

Inside my skull something like a hot poker burns my brain. It's like an ice cream headache from Satan himself. I blink my eyes. Staring down at my hands I try to bring them into focus. I wiggle my fingers, reconnecting my body with my brain. I feel the never-ending pain in my left foot. I look back at the tire and I feel my body's smallness, its feebleness next to it. I recognize my insignificance in this world.

My old life before this one is nothing but a dream. The twenty years I've lived before, the two and half years spent in the Army Reserves, stretched out over a lifetime are now compressed into a few bright flashes of recollections. I wonder about the events that led me here. It is what I wanted, but it has somehow become a punishment, a sentence for a crime. I run down the list of crimes I've committed at home and in the Army.

I think I know why I've been banished from my own company to work here. A couple of months ago when Sergeant Bennett ordered me to hop on a forklift, I told her I had no license, no training. She told me to shut my mouth and do as I was ordered. I crashed the forklift into a German cargo truck parked outside the warehouse and got my ass hauled down to the MP station.

Facing demotion, an Article 15, or even a bad conduct discharge, Sergeant Bennett gloated that I would finally get what I had coming. I was guilty, it seemed, of something, although I did not know what. The MP, a big burly man who looked like he was about to bust the seams of his BDUs, handed me a pen and paper and told me to write what happened. So I did. I wrote everything, including the part where I was ordered to hop on the forklift. My hand trembled as I signed it. When the MP read it, he said if that's what really happened, then that changed things. I am not sure exactly what changed except about a week later I was issued a back-dated license and some nasty looks from my superiors and even my comrades who worked up front. Nothing was ever said again about my punishment or even the accident, but I wasn't too stupid to understand one way or another I would pay for that and whatever else I was guilty of.

While my superiors never mentioned the incident again, I don't think they ever forgot it. Or forgave it. It wasn't long after that incident that Sergeant Bluff sent me next door to 316th to work in this warehouse for ninety days. The official reasoning was that our sister company was short soldiers, so they asked Sergeant Bluff if he could spare some bodies. He obliged, giving them Low and me. He said I could use some extra training in my job. Perhaps if he wasn't tasking me for police call or CQ duty, I would be more proficient in my Ninety-Two Alpha MOS.

"Why are you over here?" I ask Low when we're installed at our new stations in Shipping and Receiving at 316th. "I mean, it's not like you need extra training. You trained me and Dale. You're going to your next duty station in a couple of months. Why does he give a shit?" He shrugs and looks away when I ask him.

. . .

In this strange, yet familiar place we stand side by side, knowing but never acknowledging what the other knows is true. It is as if we've just stepped through the looking glass. I feel like I'm suffering from some sort of three-dimensional dyslexia. The tables, computer stations, and storage units are exact replicas of those in our warehouse but somehow look out of place. Computers are facing the wrong way, tables line the wrong wall, or a row of storage units is short. In this new company we're in our old section, shipping and receiving, in the back. There's still the big open bay, forklifts plugged in, humming on the back wall, plastic strips covering bay doors on the right wall leading to the outside where trucks are offloaded, and another, identical door on the opposite wall, with a ramp leading to outside storage.

"Does this place feel weird to you?" I ask, breaking the long silence at last.

"I don't know. It's just another SSA in the Army. All these warehouses are the same." He shrugs. "What do you mean?"

"It's different over here." I make a point of looking around. "Don't you get a weird feeling?"

"You must be talking about the platoon." A stocky, boyish-looking soldier walks across the bay and throws up his hand at Low. "Hey, man." Low lifts his chin, then nods.

"How did you know that dude before we came over here?" I ask.

"Oh," he says, "we met right when I first got here. He was cracking jokes in the line at the chow hall. We started talking and found out we come from the same place and we're both Ninety-Two Alphas."

"Wow." A slight amount of jealousy comes out despite my attempts to hide it. "Seems like you've settled in here nicely. You've got a whole new set of friends."

"Eh. I make friends wherever I go." He smiles his cheeky grin at me. "I think most people over here are a good group. They're a little different than where we come from next door."

"That's what I'm talking about." I look across the bay at two female soldiers carrying pink hard helmets toward the forklifts. One woman has her light brunette hair in low twiggy pigtails, the other has two afro puffs pulled just above her ears. "Everything is weird here. Like, look right there." I nod toward the women. "First of all, Sergeant Bluff would never let us females wear our hair like that. Can you imagine the ass-chewing if we didn't have it in a bun or a straightened bob?" My voice rises in direct proportion to my swelling anger. "Second of all, what the hell? There are females who work in the back and actually drive forklifts? They say I'm a shitty driver after that accident with the German truck, but I'm still the only female in our SSA who'll get her ass on a forklift."

"You can't listen to what they say. Sergeant Bennett and the rest of those tricks need to get their asses on a forklift so they can see it's not that easy."

"Oh, my God." I grab my sides. "I can't believe you call our squad leader a freaking trick."

"Well..." He smiles wide. "Forget them. Sergeant Bluff thinks he's punishing us by putting us on extra duty, making us work in the back and even sending us over here, but we can't look at it like that. Everything they do to us, I just look at it as an opportunity. If you think of it as a punishment, then he wins." He stares at me with his warm, brown eyes. "Being sent over here to 316th is like being given three months free leave. Look how laid back they are, look how everyone gets along here."

I look at some soldiers wiggling their hips to the hip-hop on the stereo as they process parts. Laughter rings out over the beats as a trooper throws her head back in response to a joke her comrade just shared. The women with the hard hats huddle in conversation with two male soldiers standing near the tire on the pallet, forming a game plan about what to do with it. There is no bickering, no name calling, no faces flushing from insults.

Sergeant Jones, the platoon sergeant, arrives in the back of the warehouse looking younger, fresher than I could ever imagine Sergeant Bluff appearing. Like the local magistrate at the county fair back home who manages to shake hands with everyone, Sergeant Jones stops to greet every soldier.

He stops in front of the table where Low and I are processing parts and looks at the stack of boxes we've already taped up for shipment. "I have to admit, I didn't know what to expect from some soldiers on loan, but you two have been working your asses off." Low nods and I wipe my brow with a dirty hand. "Sergeant Bluff said he was going to give me two of his best men, excuse me, soldiers." He grins at me. "I guess I really will owe him one now. I almost hate to ask if I can't have you both a little longer. I really thought I would have some more soldiers by now, but I'll see what he says."

Low and I exchange a look as Sergeant Jones walks away. My brain sizzles imagining Sergeant Bluff saying Low and I were his best soldiers. "Well, if that ain't some Grade A horseshit," I say. Low raises his eyebrows. "Platoon sergeants are such fucking politicians."

"Come on, Burton," Low says. "Why you got to be so negative? Sergeant Jones is a good guy. He's not like Sergeant Bluff."

"Whatever. I'm not being negative. I'm being a realist. He may be a good guy compared to Sergeant Bluff, but I don't trust any of these guys in charge."

"The Army's a game. It's how you play it."

"I'm trying to play the game, but it's kind of hard when I don't know the rules."

I try to make sense of all the doublespeak, the backdoor deals, and the trades that go on in the Army. Nothing can be taken as truth. I realize I don't know shit about anything except how bizarre the universe is.

When I first joined the Army I felt like the reader, writer, and main character of my own book. It was pretty straight forward, not too dramatic. I would do this, that, then this, maybe that as I galloped toward a happy ending. I was in control and I made all the choices and I would determine where my story took me.

Since I arrived in Germany, it's as if I'm some character in a Choose Your Own Adventure book. Sergeant Bluff must have read those same books about fucked-up societies, time-traveling to the future, and encounters with aliens and UFOs. Like I did with the *Choose Your Own Adventure* books, Sergeant Bluff in life marks each page where he's given a choice, (a) turn to page two or (b) turn to page thirty-six. If he doesn't like what happens on page two, he can go back to where he marked, and choose (b) to take him to page thirty-six. He can return to every place that calls for a decision and try again. He can send the main character on one ill-fated journey after another. He keeps going back, trying to figure out which choice to make to get a happy ending, but it's useless.

Across the bay my eyes search for the clock that should be on the wall, the one that is in our warehouse, but it isn't hanging here. Instead I stare down at my wristwatch. It was my first real watch, a fifteenth birthday present from Mom, that shows the sun and moon in a window on the face. The leather strap wore away in AIT, so I replaced it with a more durable yet stylish metal one that looks good when I roll the sleeves up on my BDU top. The sun is just setting in the little window, telling me it is almost time to leave and join back up with my own company for final formation. My ninety days are almost up. It is time for me to take control and help myself. I walk up to the front office, the one in the middle just like in our warehouse next door that Sergeant Bluff summoned me to. I find the base directory, I pick up the phone. I ask to make an appointment with a JAG attorney.

Chapter 10

Shitbag

"Shitbag." The word rolls off Sergeant Bennett's full lips with such obvious pleasure this August morning. Her face cannot hide the release, the ecstasy, she feels after holding it in for so long. She says the word again and again since the first time brought so much joy. Her body quivers, but she needs more. My sins must be made public. I must be made to suffer, yes, but I must also confess, beg, plead, and ask for her forgiveness. Perhaps then things will go back to how they are supposed to be, instead of this nightmare.

But I refuse to accept it. This is not my reality. I, Burton, cannot be a Shitbag.

In Basic I knew so-called Shitbags. I had never heard the name before, but a drill sergeant bestowed it upon a couple guys. One recruit came to formation every day with his Kevlar helmet and equipment belt on backwards. Another Private accidentally bloodied the head of a drill sergeant with the butt of his M-16 on the range. A soldier who refused to shower for a solid week awoke to his comrades scrubbing him with toilet bowl brushes. But they didn't last halfway through training before they were kicked out of the Army for not being "soldier material". They all were bestowed the same name—Shitbag. That is not who I am.

"You fucking Shitbag," Sergeant Bennett shouts at me. My world goes black.

If only the paperwork SNAFU hadn't occurred, and I had gone to my original assignment to 316th Transportation instead of this company. But the paperwork was wrong and Sergeant Bluff intervened. I seem to be a perpetual fuck-up. When I had gone to see the JAG attorney if only I had been able to convince him that my sanity, my well-being, even my life, depends on a transfer. Instead he told me there was nothing he could do for me, that I had to accept my assignment and that the Army puts soldiers where they need them, not where they want to go.

If only life had been different in so many ways. If only, if only, if only. I want to scream the words.

This morning the big hand on my little watch told my future. Private Dix and I were in deep shit. It was all my fault. My appetite, my hunger, my inability to control my urges would be our end. Our whole platoon would already be gathered at the warehouse, trying not to sleep through another Thursday morning Sergeant Time training on some subject like map reading or how to apply camouflage while I waited in line for breakfast.

We attempted to make up for lost time by running full speed through the warehouse. With our rucksacks smacking our backs, Kevlar helmets swinging in hand, and ammo belts bouncing around our waists, we arrived in Shipping and Receiving out of breath and sweaty, but still late. I was surprised to find the platoon seated in a circle of chairs instead of standing like we usually did. Ammo belts were draped over the backs of chairs, rucksacks were tucked under seats, and M-16s were propped between legs. Sergeant Bluff sat nodding off next to Sergeant Bennett, who was a pale shade of green. In her lap she held an open notebook and she droned on in the voice of a child just learning to read.

Dix and I stood before the group, trying to catch our breath. Soldiers stared at us with sleep and boredom on their faces. Sergeant Bennett looked up from her book, then over at Sergeant Bluff.

"She's your soldier," he said. "She was late to your Sergeant Time's training. Light her up." My eyes followed him as he stood up and walked away.

"Where were you two?" Sergeant Bennett asked.

Dix started, "Sergeant, we…"

"Not you, Dix," she said, still glaring at me. "I want to hear what she has to say."

"Sergeant, I…" I hesitated to speak the shameful words. "I was at the Burger King."

"Your ass is down at the Burger King," she said as I stood unshouldering my rucksack, "while we're all up here starving. We didn't get breakfast. Your ass don't need to be down at the Burger King when you can't even pass a PT test."

"I did pass my PT test, Sergeant," I said, calling her out on her bullshit. I held back calling her out on the unfairness of not being able to get breakfast because the lines at both Burger King and the chow hall are too long. I rolled my eyes and let my rucksack fall into the crook of my elbow.

"Shut your mouth." She waved her hand at me. "And keep your rucksack on your back. Hold on to your M-16. I think you need to burn off some of those extra calories. As your new squad leader I say your PT hasn't been looking that good."

I sucked on my bottom lip.

"I think you have a discipline problem." She threw the book from her lap to the floor where it landed with a smack. "We were all just talking about you the other day, about how we should teach you to show some more respect."

"Respect, Sergeant?" I asked. "When was the last time I got respect? I'm a Specialist, but Sergeant Bluff stands Privates to my right in formation and says they outrank me. Over the last eight months he's put me on every CQ duty. I always get tasked to clean latrines, for police call..." Lemske and Peterson snickered.

"We've been trying to train you." Her face sagged. "When you start acting like a Specialist, you'll be treated like one."

"Train me, Sergeant?" I laughed. "Like when I got sent next door to Three-Sixteen? What did I do wrong? Why do I need so much training? Where's my counseling statement?"

"You want a counseling statement? I can give you a counseling statement." Her voice vibrated off the rafters. "I'll tell you what you've done wrong, though. You have no respect for your NCOs. You have gone on profile again for your ankle. You game the system. You let everyone else up here do your job while you go to Burger King and sick-call."

"I'm at work, Sergeant, every day. One time I was late."

"I thought I told you to keep your mouth shut," she said. "And, no, it wasn't one time. There was that time you were late with Low."

That time last spring when Low and I were late returning from lunch resulted in our mowing bare ground for hours after Final Formation. I still can't believe he's gone. He was my best friend, here one minute and the next gone. He's off to some God-Awful duty station in Texas, though I can't imagine anywhere worse than here. Before he left, we shared an awkward hug in the barracks hallway, exchanged addresses, and promised to stay in touch. I told myself I didn't care, I didn't need anyone, and I never let myself get close to anyone. Now, however, there's a big gaping wound left by his absence. The only consolation is he isn't here to see my massacre.

. . .

Sergeant Bennett looked at me. "You can go ahead and put your rucksack down. I can't concentrate on training, and I think we all need a little break since you already had yours." She directed her gaze at Dix, who was still standing beside me. "Dix, come over here and sit down. None of this is your fault. This is on her. Burton kidnapped you and held you hostage. She fucked you over. She's not your friend."

Wearing a relieved expression, he plopped down into an empty seat next to Dale.

"Everyone," Sergeant Bennett said, "come in here closer. Make a circle." The sound of chairs moving across the concrete was like chewing on aluminum foil. I shut my eyes to the noise.

"Get over there." I opened my eyes to see Sergeant Bennett pointing toward the center. "Get your ass over in the middle. Leave your rucksack, but bring your M-16. We're going to have a little pow-wow. You're going to do some PT while we all have a talk."

I walked to the center of the circle.

"Start with some push-ups. Assume the front leaning rest position."

I went down on my hands and knees, then stuck my feet out behind me and leveled my back. I placed my rifle across the backs of my hands like I had learned in Basic, to keep the muzzle up out of the filth.

"Put the M-16 across your back," she said. "I better not see you let it drop."

On one hand I balanced my body and with the other I positioned the weapon, its butt on the floor and barrel across my back.

"Burton," she said. "You want to know what you've done wrong? Why don't I let your comrades tell you what they think, hmm?"

I turned my head to glance at my sergeant.

"Get on your back, do some flutter kicks," she said.

I grabbed my rifle and bounced to my feet like a gymnast doing a dismount, then rolled onto my back and stuck my feet in the air. The M-16 balanced across my abdomen. "Is this high enough, Sergeant?" I asked.

She ignored me and instead directed a question toward the other soldiers. "Is there something specific you'd like to talk to me about? Because if there is," she lowered her voice as if she didn't want me to hear, "and you're worried about her saying something to you, don't be. I've ordered her to keep her mouth closed. So if you want to tell me something, now is your chance."

I smiled despite the sweat dripping into my eyes. I haven't done anything to anyone. No one, except maybe Lemske, Peterson or Horne, who hate everyone anyway, would be enough of a buddy-fucker to make shit up about me. Besides, in the Army there's an unwritten rule that you don't whine to leadership about your problems since their meddling would make shit worse.

"Come on," Sergeant Bennett said.

"Well," a male soldier said. I didn't recognize the voice and from my position on the floor, and I couldn't see his face. "Well, it's like you said, Sergeant. She's late sometimes. Like today. It's not fair." I cocked my head to see his face.

"Roll." Sergeant Bennett barked at my head. "Roll right, then roll left until I tell you to stop. Stop looking over here."

I held my M-16 in my outstretched hands and put my belly on the floor. I prioritized keeping the muzzle of my rifle out of the soot at the expense of the rest of my body, including my face. I balanced it on my arms while I rolled and held my head up as long as I could. My neck and shoulders quivered and burned. I gave up and ate dirt.

Sergeant Bennett laughed. "Right," she said, trying to regain her composure. "What else?"

"She always be on profile." Lemske's voice was unmistakable. Even though she often adopted what she thought was cool—

Army speak—she never quite shook her WASPY New England accent. "She think she entitled," she continued. "She think she can come in here from college and not have to work."

"That is such utter fucking bullshit." I got up on my knees. I stared at Lemske. I started to blurt out how she was regurgitating Sergeant Bluff's tired lines about me, but I was interrupted before I could spit out the words.

"Since you're up, do some lunges," Sergeant Bennett said. "And I'm not going to warn you again about keeping your mouth shut. You're not a part of this conversation."

"It's just like you said, Sergeant," Peterson chimed in. "She's doesn't have any respect."

"Maybe she needs an Article 15 in addition to her counseling statement, what do you think?" Sergeant Bennett asked. "Bust her down to Private for real and take away her money. Confine her ass to post and give her extra duty for forty-five days. She's been having too much fun over here in Germany. That's not what the Army is about. Y'all work hard. Y'all are disciplined. Y'all shouldn't have to pick up her slack."

"Hooah!" a choir of voices cried out.

I lowered my head and rifle.

"And what else about her?" Sergeant Bennett asked.

"Look at her," Horne said, gesturing toward me. Peterson snorted.

"What's wrong with her?" Sergeant Bennett asked, feigning ignorance as if she wasn't ready to fire off a list of things she considered wrong with me. "Is it her uniform or her boots? What are you talking about, Horne?"

"Yeah," he paused, before continuing. "Her uniform could use some improvement, but it's just the way she looks in general. Especially her hair." His voice snarled as he spoke. "She's dyed it, I don't know what color red you call that. Why do females get away with what they get away with?"

"I could definitely write her up for having a faddish hairstyle," Sergeant Bennett said.

"She ugly," he said. The audience broke out in laughter. "I mean, I'm just being honest."

Everyone's eyes turned to look at my flushed, sweaty face and dirty trembling hands to confirm that Horne was right. I, however, was not unaware of Horne's low opinion of my looks. A couple of months ago, during a breast-feeding discussion with new moms Specialists McKenzie and Kerns, he had crossed his arms across his round belly and stared at my chest. He had declared that any kid of mine would starve to death if I didn't bottle feed it.

"Get on your back," Sergeant Bennett said. "Do some more flutter kicks."

"She only wants to look German because she's always got some German dude up in the barracks," Horne continued.

I dropped my heels to the floor. "You fat fuck," I muttered.

"Wait, what?" Sergeant Bennett asked Horne. "She's got German men up in the barracks? How did I not know about this?" A hush fell over the platoon in response to the seriousness of the allegations. "I should report this to Sergeant Bluff. Did y'all report this? She's bringing German men, who y'all don't even know, up where y'all live?"

"Hmm-hmm," Lemske and Peterson said in unison. "We know," Lemske said.

"This is ridiculous," Specialist McKenzie spoke up from the crowd. "Y'all trying to make it sound like she's bringing serial killers in with her. She has a boyfriend who is German." Her face was filled with so much pity that I couldn't bear to look at her.

"Shut the fuck up McKenzie," Horne said. "You would defend her. You're a fucking Shitbag yourself."

"I'm just saying," she shrugged, "you can't keep picking on

people and expect them not to snap. One of these days it's going to happen."

"Like how we all said you were going to go nuts one day and burn down the warehouse since you hated the Army so much?"

"We know Burton doesn't have the guts to do anything like that, although..." Sergeant Bennett scrunched up her face like she smelled hot garbage. "I knew she was a dirty bird, but I never thought she would fuck a nasty German. They're not even circumcised." Peterson and Lemske's faces lit up and leaned in closer. "What does she see in them?"

"Probably because she knows no American man would have her," Horne joined in the conversation.

It was okay for American guys to date German girls, but not American girls to go out with German dudes, I guess. I stopped my flutter kicks and stared at Horne. He bragged about his sexploits with European girls he brought back to his room. He claimed if American girls wanted to be treated right, then we needed to learn how to fuck a man right, the way a German girl does. The women of our platoon said the only girls he got were the poor, desperate, underage German chicks he paid for with American dollars and Mountain Dew.

Sweat oozed from every crevice and dripped down my back and legs, even between my boobs squashed flat in a sports bra. It was like a thousand ants crawling over my entire body and I was helpless to swat them away. Still on my back from doing flutter kicks, I dropped my head to the ground and howled with laughter. I held my sides and stomped my boots into the floor.

"That's great, Horne," I said. "That's a good one. You really ought to be a comedian."

"Goddamn," he muttered. "Mackenzie's right. She's snapped."

"Stand up," Sergeant Bennett said. "Let me see if you've had enough."

I stood up to face my judge and jury.

"God look at you." She shook her head. Some other soldiers snickered. "You look like you've been rolling around in shit. You look like the Shitbag you really are."

I stared at her without blinking.

"I don't think you've had enough." She laughed. "Get down and beat your face."

My nerves fired and my muscles twitched. My bones ached. My body was encoding and remembering every word, every insult hurled at it since my arrival. I struggled to get down into the push-up position on the floor. I rolled over so I could put the M-16 on my back again and I collapsed into a heap. I feel the tears, but I will them not to come. I refuse to give them what they want. They will never break me, no matter how hard they try.

"Dale." Sergeant Bennett's voice called my buddy's name.

Dale and I had been friends from the moment I arrived, although at times I sensed he didn't approve of Low and me sharing jokes or stories just between us. Nevertheless, the three of us always went to chow together, hung out at the pizza place near the PX after work, and stayed out too late dancing to techno at the club. Dix arrived, and it was still three of us, working in the back of the warehouse, hanging out in our free time, like when Low was here.

"Dale." Our sergeant's voice was more urgent this time.

"Yes, Sergeant." Dale's voice sounded like a robot waking up and responding to its master's commands.

"What do you say, Dale?"

I registered only the first word Dale said, "She..."

An explosion went off inside my head and my ears began to ring. My vision turned red, then black. The noise and lights going off in my brain drowned out almost everything except Sergeant Bennett's roar, the other soldiers howling, even Dale's chuckle. I knew what he said, even if I didn't.

"Shitbag." Now I hear that word dripping off Sergeant Bennett's tongue. I hear it echoed from other soldiers. I am ordered to silence, but I can't—I can't anything anymore.

"Aaagh." I make some gurgling noise, like I'm choking or drowning in my own blood or tears. "Fuck all y'all," I say, finally articulating. I pull myself to my knees and then to my feet. Sweat drips off my face, my eyes water, spit foams at the corners of my mouth. I look at my friend and spit the words in his direction. "And especially fuck you, Dale. You can go to hell." The laughter stops. Sergeant Bennett's eyes widen. Everyone turns to look at me. My rifle trembles in my hands. "You ain't nothing but a fucking Shitbag, just like me."

Dale stares down between his feet. Red welts form across his face as if I have bitch-slapped him with my words.

"Well," Sergeant Bennett says, smiling.

"I'm done," I say.

"You're done?" she asks. "Why do you think I should stop smoking your ass? It's up to me to decide when you're done. What are you going to say to convince me to stop?"

The muscles in my body tremble and I go back down my hands and knees. I bow down before my rifle and hide my face. "I want to see the Chaplain."

Now, I throw myself at the mercy of God and the Army. The word Shitbag echoes throughout the warehouse and my head. Every square inch of me, my uniform, my face, my hands, are coated with a black soot like that which covered my uncle after a day in the Eastern Kentucky coal mines. His dust, though, he wore proud like a badge of honor. My dust carries on it the word Shitbag and drapes itself over me for my comrades to see. I will wear it. I confess to what I am, but it is not for others to forgive me.

CHAPTER 11

BUTTERFLIES AND BULLSHIT

Maybe it's these long warm days, even here in Bavaria, that remind me of the same summer days growing up on Stinking Creek Holler. Maybe it's the blacktop outside this Army warehouse sizzling in the sun. Maybe back home is somewhere I'll always see no matter where I go.

Before my eyes it is a painting come to life.

I watch as little me, only eight or nine, steps off the hot blacktop and onto the parched clay dirt road that cut through Papaw's farm. I kick off my little pink flip flops. I don't need them on the banks of the creek. A Monarch butterfly flutters across my line of vision, carrying off my plans to look for crawdads and mud turtles. I veer off the sunlit path and into the dried puddles near the barn. Careful not to get juiced, I crawl under the electric fence and into the pasture. I scan the sky for the butterfly and the ground for cow patties.

The butterfly waits for me to catch up. It pauses on its journey to double back and do a mid-air dance. After finishing its performance, it crosses the field, its wings glistening under the bright sun. Spreading my arms out to my sides, I make a propeller noise with my lips and home in on my target. My imagination bounces from storyline to storyline as I ponder if the butterfly will lead me to a secret garden or into the hands of enemy combatants.

The Monarch speeds up, eyeing its destination, as I follow close behind. It descends into the dark, mucky ground near the barn. Coming up on its landing spot, I stare down with equal measure fascination and disgust. The butterfly flaps its wings, lulling on a fresh pile of cow dung. I turn to walk away, but I can't take my eyes off the butterfly. It seems even more beautiful, its wings almost luminescent, against the hot pile of brown mess.

These memories chase me through the remaining August days in the back of the hot, airless warehouse. After final formation I waste no time shaking off the memories, tearing off my grimy BDUs, and changing into something else. Just outside Gate 3 past the guards, Markus, my new guy, waits for me. On the sidewalk, he sits on his small yellow scooter. "Ein Roller," he calls it, in his native German, rolling his r's. It's a small 50cc, like one I used to have as a teen. Although now reduced to pillion, I don't mind squeezing up behind and holding on tight.

He greets me with a kiss and a, "Hallo." I throw my bag under the seat, grab the extra helmet, and hop on the back. As if riding on some two-wheeled bumblebee, we zip through the ancient streets of Bimbleberg, cutting off BMWs and Volkswagens, blowing through amber traffic lights before they turn red, and squeezing past parked cars on narrow cobblestone streets. We ride until we reach a city park near the center of town. Jumping off the scooter I remove my helmet and shake out my choppy red layers.

"Mein Gott," I say. "I thought Germans followed the rules."

Markus gives me a concerned look until I smile. His cheeks dimple, and he shrugs.

In the park, we stroll hand in hand through trees and past butterflies landing on wildflowers. We pause on a footbridge, admiring the stucco houses with red roofs dotting the banks of the Reigen River, before making our way down a meandering path toward a bench under a towering tree. He tells me bits and pieces about the town, its history, even how his own family has lived here for centuries. I listen, trying to make sense of a language and a culture I don't fully comprehend. It is as if Bimbleberg, Germany, even Markus has always existed. I realize all of them will be here after I'm gone, even after the U.S. Army has packed up and left.

I've tried to keep his world of Germany separate from mine, the Army and where I come from in Eastern Kentucky. He has never seen me in my uniform, he hears only an "American" accent, he sees my bright red hair I bought out of a box of German hair dye. He hasn't heard what my sergeant or even folks back home say about me.

"I'm from Kentucky," I say, a lump forming in my throat. I admire the quietness in his profile, his chest rising and sinking, as he stares out. The river gurgles, birds hop along the ground in search of a snack, and the last of the flowers bloom in the fading sunlight.

"Yes." He faces me. He squeezes my hand and grins. "Kentucky whiskey. Kentucky Fried Chicken." I roll my eyes at what passes for a joke between our two cultures.

"Zurück in mein heim in Kentucky," I say in my mix of bad German and English. "Before the Army, before here." I pause, thinking what I will say next. "I went to University. I studied Psychology."

"Wow," he says. "You are smart."

His cobalt eyes grow large and bright. For a moment I hate him for looking at me with so much tenderness, for thinking I am smart. If I were a good person, I'd cut him loose, let him find someone better than me. When I look at him, with his messy dark helmet hair, his smooth skin, and his beautiful eyes, I can't. I am selfish.

"I used to paint and write and read." I want to shut up, not waste what little free time I have from the Army, but I can't. I pull at a tall piece of grass, tearing it from its roots. "When I get out of the Army, I'll go back to Uni. I won't always be a hillbilly or a Shit-bag." My words are an unbroken string of English syllables. Markus nods. His blank, polite smile tells me he doesn't fully *verstehe*—understand.

"I was not so good in school," he laughs. "I did not go to Uni. I go to work with heat."

I give him a confused look. He mimes and tries words in both English and German. From my bag I pull out my pocket German-English dictionary. He points out various entries, until at last I give up, smile, and lie, "Ah, yes. Ich verstehe."

Although we have been dating all summer, we don't have much conversation. We have spent afternoons in beer gardens, evenings dancing, nights in each other's arms. There has been no need to cross the language barrier. I don't even know what he does for work. All I know is he is eighteen, kind, and with his dark-hair and high cheekbones, every time I look at him my heart flutters. Perhaps that is all I want to know about him. He doesn't know much about me, either. It isn't necessary.

"Come." He stands and extends his hand in an almost formal invitation. "We watch the sun." He leads me back to the bridge and to a golden sun setting over the river. He asks if I want to go back to base. In broken German I say, "No, I never want to go back." He wraps his arms around me. I exhale and the tension from my body releases as tears.

We stand on the bridge long enough to watch the moon replace the sun. Lights from distant houses dance on the blue-black surface of the water. Leaning over the bridge, I dangle my arms off the railing. I feel the moist air licking at my face. Markus grabs my arm and pulls me back.

"I just want to look," I say, shooting him a mischievous grin before looking back over the water. My myopic eyes swirl the colors into something beautiful yet tragic. My arms get goosebumps and a chill comes over me. Markus and I are like two figures in the foreground of a Van Gogh painting. The moon, the lights, the river are like an artist's perfectly rendered brushstrokes on a canvas. When I close my eyes, I can smell the oils.

Markus draws me back close to him. Brushing my cheek with his hand he says, "Du bist so schön. Ich liebe dich." I tremble. "You are so beautiful," repeating in English, he says, perhaps thinking I will better understand, but I already do. "I love you."

I close my eyes and shake my head.

CHAPTER 12

PRIVATE PARTS

I won't be Specialist Burton today. Today I will be someone else. An American expat, a study abroad student, or maybe even a German girl.

Outside, the promising blue skies of the morning have given way to a sad, gray September afternoon. There can be no doubt that today, not the calendar, marks the true beginning of autumn. Like the Germans, I have learned to not let the threat of bad weather keep me at home. I will wear my slick black pleather jacket, in case it rains, over my pink three-quarter sleeve turtle neck and carry my umbrella I bought to go with my black purse. I will go with my stacked-heeled, zip-up fake leather booties. To finish off my outfit I will wear gray, not black, trousers. The gray pants and pink top will keep the outfit from being too serious for a Sunday afternoon at a sidewalk cafe with my friend Mara.

I run mousse through the choppy layers of my bright red hair. I apply some light makeup. I need a little eyeliner and some cover-up to hide the angry rash of zits on my chin and forehead brought on by wearing my cap and helmet with its chinstrap. Nothing too outlandish like the glitter eyeshadow I favor for nights going out dancing at the club. I won't worry about walking in heels despite my throbbing ankle. My injured foot hurts too much today to walk the distance to the bus stop, so I will drive and hope for close parking. I text Mara, ask her if she wants me to pick her up or meet her at the cafe.

I think about how we met last spring at Hermano's, the Mexican restaurant/bar in downtown Bimbleberg. When a group of German college students bounced in time to the electronic pulses of Daft Punk over the club's stereo system, we found ourselves pushed together against a back wall. We rolled our eyes, fanned our faces, and laughed, shouting to one another over the music something about how hot it was and the absurdity of the crowd. I mimed that I wanted to get a drink and nodded in her direction to ask if she did, too. "Ja," she said.

I sharpened up my Army riot-control skills and what I learned from being in a mosh pit once at a Stone Temple Pilots concert in Louisville. I put out my arms, shoved through some drunk Europeans, and made a hole so my new friend and I could get to the bar. In no time at all we were rehydrating with two shots of silver tequila, a daiquiri for her, and a Desperado beer for me. When the music died down, we introduced ourselves. She told me she was a student who lived in town with her family. My limited German at last gave away my identity as an American. "Ich bin Soldatin," I said. I am a soldier—feminine noun.

"Yeah?" Mara smiled. "Really? A soldier? Cool."

When I have had too much to drink or too much to think, I wonder if Mara and I should be friends at all. Tall and gorgeous, with waves of blonde hair falling down her back, she is too pretty to be my friend. Although she is seventeen, the same age I was when I went to the Army three years ago, perhaps she is also too young.

I rationalize our friendship by telling myself that if beautiful people want to hang out with me, then there must be something pretty about me. I tell myself that she is old enough to hang out with me, a soldier, since when I was her age I was already a soldier myself.

I hear myself saying these things and wonder if I'm any better than my male comrades who justify their relationships with underage girls. "German chicks are so much more mature than American girls their age," they say. "Plus, they're freaking hot."

Sometimes I think I should break off our friendship. Being around me is dangerous. She gets ideas in her head. She asks if I will bring her on base, if I will introduce her to some of my guy friends. She wants to meet a handsome American soldier like in the movies, "like Tom Cruise in *Top Gun*." She wants to get married, move to the United States, have a house, have babies.

I tell her that's a nice story, but that's not reality. I tell her to stay far away from soldiers. I tell her they spend all their money on beer and cars and girls. She laughs and says as long as he loves her. I can't shatter her fairy tale. I can't tell her the darker side. I can't tell her about how a soldier will meet a girl in a foreign land, tell the girl how beautiful she is, tell her he loves her. Then after he gets bored, when he's got what he wanted, he'll call her a Barracks Rat, and "give" her to his buddy, a new soldier, to "break him into Germany".

I can't say that I know because not long ago I stayed up all night, consoling a comrade's fling who found out my friend had used her and was handing her off to the next soldier. The girl, Mara's age, maybe a year younger, sobbed in my arms and I gave her Smirnoff, the only thing I knew to ease her pain. She begged me for answers I didn't have. "He's your friend. You're a soldier, too. Can't you talk to him? He said he loved me, but he wants me to fuck this other friend. I love him, not his friend. Why does he do this to me?"

I wonder if Mara is yet old enough to understand real life. Then there are other times, when I am certain she knows more than I ever will. When I told her I was going in the fall to Poland on a NATO training mission, the first American troops since World War II, she told me when she was a little girl her family immigrated from Poland to Germany when it was still two countries.

She insists she doesn't recall much from her former life there. Blowing a lock of hair out of her face, she gets a faraway look in her eyes. Her face grows tired and sad, like she has been asked to carry too much for too long. With her brows furrowed and mouth drawn, she looks like she knows more than most girls her age. I see it then, that her beauty comes from strength and determination, not from youthful naivete. She catches me staring, then smiles, as if embarrassed. In our bastardized mix of English and German, I ask her, "What is wrong?" "Nichts." She shakes her head. "Nothing."

Before heading out to meet Mara, I check my reflection in my Army-issued barracks mirror one last time. My face is pale. My eyes stare back at me, cold and unblinking, as if they've looked into a future they can't forget, attempt a smile, but without the eyes' cooperation it is an obvious fake. My once full lips form a thin line across my face. I put on some lipstick, hoping to color in a hint of a smile. I dab on a little more blush to imitate the colors of lost youth. I reline my eyes, hoping to camouflage the truth threatening to reveal itself.

Pausing by my barracks door, I rest my palm on the door handle and listen. I have learned to wait until it is safe to leave, for the noise in the hallway to die down. Then almost on impulse, I grab my Gerber multi-tool from the top of my bookcase and toss it in my purse. I tremble, thinking about who it is I'm protecting myself from. I can't even remember when this habit started. Was it a week ago, a month ago?

. . .

Not long ago, as I pushed a cart of supplies through the warehouse, Sergeant Bluff stepped into my path.

"Do you think I don't know what goes on in my own platoon, in my own barracks? I know what every one of my soldiers does. There's not a single place on this post or in this town you can go that I don't know about."

His steely brown eyes burrowed into my own wide blue eyes.

"I have my people watching you, I know everything you do."

He said nothing else on the matter. He walked away and left me to finish my work. I racked my brain trying to recall what I had done over the weekend that might have brought this on. Maybe someone saw my boyfriend Markus leaving my room. Maybe Sergeant Bluff saw me returning with some bags from a shopping trip to Nürnberg. Maybe someone saw me with my hair done, my makeup on, and wearing my new outfit as I got into my car.

If I was going to escape whoever was tailing me, I was going to have to separate my Army life from my life in Germany. My German friends and boyfriend would have to stay off-post. I would have to become someone else, separate from a soldier, from Burton, when I saw them. I would transform myself any time I stepped outside this base into the German world, no matter if it was to sight-see, shop, or sip coffee.

I cut my hair into a pixie cut that I combed down for duty and styled with mousse after-hours. Clingy knit tops, slacks, and heels replaced the hoodies, Adidas sneakers, and jeans I wore for running errands on base. I practiced makeup techniques, playing with lipstick, eyeliner, even glitter, until I was satisfied I no longer resembled Burton.

Sometimes when the lights are off in the hallway of the barracks, I stroll past my own comrades. They give me puzzled looks, sometimes even a, "Hallo. Gruss Gott." I look familiar, but they can't place me. They think I'm a new German girlfriend/Barracks Rat they haven't met. I feel exotic, beautiful, disgusting, and a bit dangerous. I feel like some double agent who's lost track of which side she's on. The adrenaline rush I get from this game, from reclaiming the private parts of my life, is more intoxicating than a shot of Jägermeister.

Sometimes, though, like today, my nerves aren't up to it. I just want to walk to my car and meet a friend like civilians do. I look under my door, but I can't tell if the hallway lights are on; there's no noise. Across the narrow street, no bigger than a sidewalk, my car is in the adjacent parking lot. I plot the course in my head, turn right out of my room, down the hall, another right out the double doors into the stairwell, down a couple flights of stairs, and out the barracks doors into the fresh air. If I double-time it, I won't have to worry about being recognized. I won't feel obliged to say hello to anyone, decipher whether inquiries of what I'm up to and where I'm going are benign.

I creak open my door and slide out. I look right, then left. With a soft click I lock it behind me. I rush down my route as planned. In what feels like the tick of a second hand on my watch, I am turning my key in the driver's side door of my BMW. I smile, thinking how once again I was able to slink out of the barracks without anyone knowing. Then, from somewhere above my head a voice booms, "Well, well, well, Burton."

As if shocked by a bolt of electricity, I jump back from the car. The blood races from my extremities and my hands go numb, causing me to fumble with my keys. I look towards the barracks. Up on the third floor, from an open window, Sergeant Bluff leans out into the gray clouds overhead. My purse drops from my shoulder to my elbow. I force a tight but polite smile.

"Where are you going all dressed up?" His smirking is obvious even from where I stand.

I glimpse down at my clothes. Flashes of pink sweater, black jacket, and slacks jumpstart the memory of my outfit. A silence fills the street between my car and the barracks. I stare up at him. I try to figure out whose room he is in, why he is in our barracks on a Sunday, and why he gives a shit about what I'm wearing.

"Nowhere, Sergeant," I answer him, saying the only thing I can think of.

"Uh-huh, I bet." His white, toothy smile glows against the darkness of the room behind him. His head bobs up and down on his shoulders. I can feel his eyes on every article of my clothing. "You going to meet a guy? You got you a little boyfriend?"

"No, Sergeant." I am covered from my neck to my toes, but still I feel stripped bare and accused. "I'm just going to meet a friend for coffee, Sergeant."

"Mmm-huh. Okay," he laughs and pulls himself back inside the window.

Inside my car, I lock the door. I straighten my rearview mirror and look for Sergeant Bluff. I still feel his eyes on me. I can almost hear him laughing. I turn around to look out the back glass. He is nowhere to be found, but I know he is always there. He always will be. I slump over the steering wheel. I try to cry, but I've dried up inside. My fingers dangle by my legs and I feel the last of my energy draining out of my fingertips. I picture my brain or heart or soul shattering into tiny pieces on the ground beside my car. Whatever makes me, me, feels disconnected from my body. I feel myself grow cold and numb as I stare into the distance. Perhaps this is death. I hope. There will be no tomorrow. There will be no more Sergeant Bluff. There will be no more Army.

My cell phone chimes, breaking the cold, dead silence inside the car. Inside my chest, my heart thumps, rushing blood through my veins to warm my body. It's Mara. She texts that she would like to ride with me to the café and she'll see me soon.

Outside my windshield the rainy, gray skies are giving way to streaks of blue. It looks like autumn might hold off for at least one more day. No doubt my friend and I will spend the rest of the day sitting side by side at a sidewalk table, drinking cappuccinos. We'll sip our coffees, then order just one more despite the expense because neither one of us will want to leave just yet. I won't tell her what I did to get out the post gates and into Bimbleberg. She won't tell me about what it took for her to get to Bimbleberg either. I won't tell her it will take even more strength to go back through those gates, become Specialist Burton again, and march off to Poland with Sergeant Bluff. I won't ask her if she, too, sometimes fears the days, the weeks, and the years to come. We'll drink coffee. We'll hide those parts of ourselves that are too private, too dark to bring into daylight.

CHAPTER 13

REAL SOLDIERS

The Polish motor pool bay has a musty, old-attic smell, like it's been boarded up and forgotten about for years. I wonder how Sergeant Bluff found this place where he has taken my buddies Dale and Dix to work the Class I food point on this NATO mission. This will be our home, where we sleep, eat, shit, and even store pallets of food for all of October, maybe even into November. Info about the length of our stay has been vague.

This place reeks of that Army stench that lingers on TA-50 gear no matter where in the world it is issued to a soldier. No one has identified what that Army smell is, but some say the fibers forever trap the dirt of the field and the blood of dead soldiers. We all bleed green in the United States Army, and judging by the smell, so does the Polish Army.

All of us must bleed for our countries. Polish men, like German men, are conscripted into the military. They have no choice—they must serve in return for whatever it is their countries provide them. My comrades and I chose, for our own individual reasons, to lay down our lives for our nation if asked. Today is our day to die, perhaps.

"You're mine, I own you," Sergeant Bluff barks as he stands before Dale, Dix, and me as we try not to shake from cold and nerves in our little formation.

The blood drains from my head and extremities. I have been standing so long at attention that I'm certain I will faint. In here there is no heat and the lights are off. Outside is a pleasant but cool October afternoon. In here is a frigid morgue. The cinder block traps the cold air. The tiny windows near the ceiling do little to let in warmth from a fading autumn sun.

Behind where I stand, an exterior bay door is open to the outside world. The warmth of the sun wraps itself around my back while darkness eclipses my front. We'll freeze to death after the sun goes down, I fear. My eyes search the room for signs of a pot-bellied stove, then I recall Sergeant Bluff not packing it. He said it wasn't needed since we weren't staying in a tent. A truck starts up behind me outside the motor pool. I look out the corner of my left eye, trying to see all the way out the back of my head. Who is here? Where is here?

"Eyes straight ahead, Burton," Sergeant Bluff says. "That's what I'm talking about. You all lack the discipline to stand at attention in formation." I stare straight ahead. "You don't even know how to be in the Army. That's why I brought you three up here."

Dale stands to my immediate right, and Dix is to his right. Except for a little tuft of blond hair circling the tops of their scalps, their heads are shaved. Dix has even adopted the elder's nervous thumb twitch. They take turns tapping and twiddling their thumbs as if they are spelling out a secret message in Morse code.

Maybe if that Shitbag incident in the warehouse hadn't happened I'd have picked up this little habit as well. After fessing up to fucking up, saying that we were sorry a few times, promising to have each other's backs from then on, and paying for my night of drinking at the club, Dale and Dix gained my forgiveness. I never forgot, but one needs allies in both the Army and in war.

"You're not really in the Army until you've been to war," Sergeant Bluff shouts at the three of us trying not to shiver. "You all have no idea what the Army is really like."

The Army, I know, is where time folds over onto itself, until you have no idea how you arrived at a place. For as long as the universe has existed, you feel as if you've been standing in a former Soviet motor pool. Your memories are the only thing reminding you of a time before.

There's no clock on the wall. Sneaking a peek at my watch with my hands tucked in the small of my back is impossible. Only by the sun's lengthening and shrinking rays across the floor can I gauge the passage of time. The minutes and hours or even days and weeks in this place shouldn't concern me. We are here, Sergeant Bluff says, until he says we can leave.

"Do you know how old I am? Do you know how many deployments and wars I've been to in my career since I enlisted at eighteen?" he asks. I look at Dale, anticipating some sort of smart-ass remark, but he is not Low. Sergeant Bluff doesn't want an answer at all. Still, I look up and attempt a calculation in my head. According to whispers among members of my unit, the combat patch he wears on his right shoulder is from the infantry unit he served with during Desert Storm. I don't know how long he has served in the Army. Some soldiers say he has been in sixteen, eighteen, almost twenty years. Since the Gulf War there has been Somalia, Bosnia, Kosovo, Macedonia, and some other so-called peace-keeping missions I can't recall. What he has seen in the last decade or longer. He is old, hardened. I try to calculate his age. Carry the one, that would make him... "Don't roll your eyes at me, Burton," he says.

"I wasn't, Sergeant," I say. He cocks his head, waiting for me to explain. "I was just..."

"You all have been in the Army a long time. Some of you are near the end of your first enlistment and you haven't seen a single deployment. You've got your rank without doing a damn thing to earn it. Hell, I didn't even earn my first promotion to Private E-2 before the Army sent me down range." He walks back and forth in front of us as if we are preparing for inspection. A cough tickles my throat, but I choke it down into my chest.

"You all are in Germany in your comfortable barracks, better than anything I ever had. Driving BMWs that me and my peers can't even afford. You've got your girlfriends and Burton's got her little boyfriend, running off to sick-call every week."

My eyes widen at hearing my name. I wonder if it would make Sergeant Bluff happy to know I'm not sure if I have a boyfriend waiting for me when I get home. Markus told me two days before I left that he didn't know if he could wait a whole month for my return from Poland. I told him he didn't love me, and he never did if he wanted to dump me before such a stressful mission. I screamed at him to get out of my room and out of my life. He started crying and begged me to let him stay. It was our last night together before I left—maybe forever.

"Y'all have had it too good. Well, that's going to change. That's why I brought you to Poland with me." With sharp laser-focus Sergeant Bluff trains his eyes on me. "You're not really soldiers, you're just Shitbags, but I'm going to turn you into soldiers. You're going to experience war."

The pretend war, played with real equipment and real soldiers, begins. The faint roar of Apache helicopters gearing up for their mock training with authentic rockets makes its way through the motor pool doors.

CHAPTER 14

FIELDSTRIPPED

Outside the rear doors of the motor pool bay, Arkey, a Polish soldier not long out of his teen years, stands against a backdrop of broken pallets and an overflowing garbage dumpster. Between his lips rests a cigarette. Smoke wafts up from the burning cherry into the frigid October night sky. He takes hold of the cigarette, inhales, throws his head back, exhales, and returns it to his lips.

Wrapping my camo Gore-Tex jacket tight, I watch, mesmerized. The scent of tobacco, which I usually find nauseating, is intoxicating. I breathe in, then out. My breath drifts up, mingling with Arkey's smoke. One whiff of his preferred national brand brings back bittersweet memories of the past month on this mock deployment. Until tonight, until I smelled the cigarette, until I realized the mission was over, that I would soon head back with the rest of my company to our Army base in Germany, I never thought I would miss anything, or anyone, here.

Against his scrubbed white face, Arkey's eyes glow bright green. At the beginning of this NATO mission, his eyes were a dull hazel, his cheeks hollow. Compared to my American comrades and me, who still had our baby fat, he looked like a tired, hungry Van Gogh figure painted as a soldier. But a steady diet of field chow has softened the hard edges of his face. His uniform, which once hung from his slender frame, now shows off his broad shoulders. He catches me watching as he straightens his royal blue beret on his sandy blond head and shoots me a crooked grin. I smile back.

Officially, he is a truck driver for the Polish Army. Unofficially, he is the Polish-English interpreter for our small logistics platoon that consists of our fearless leader, Sergeant Bluff, my two buddies, Specialist Dale and Private Dix, and me, Specialist Burton, the only woman. Officially, unofficially, he has become another logistical specialist, working with our Army to complete our supply mission.

Our platoon sergeant either didn't know or didn't care that he needed more than a handful of soldiers to supply the thousands of NATO troops on this exercise. We were understaffed and overwhelmed from day one. Although I can blame Sergeant Bluff for that, I do not know who to blame for failing to see that we would need someone to translate between American troops and the Polish soldiers delivering our supplies. Fortunately for us, Arkey stepped forward. He announced he was fluent in German, English, and Polish, with a working knowledge of Russian. Sergeant Bluff told him English and Polish would suffice. Later, he recognized Arkey's labor was just as valuable to us as his language skills.

One morning, Sergeant Bluff called to me after our daily briefing. Starting at the top of my head, his eyes moved over my face, down my shoulders to my torso. He let them linger on my chest, belly, and hips. His gaze advanced down my shins to the toes of my boots. He then snorted and drew back his head. When his dark eyes again met mine, behind them I saw his mind working out the contradictions. Whatever it was about me that repulsed him also attracted him.

"Get outside and find your little Polack friend," Sergeant Bluff ordered. "Tell him if he isn't translating, then he needs to find another way to make himself useful to the United States Army. Let him know he needs to get off his lazy ass and go to work or else he can go back to wherever he came from."

I translated my NCO's words into a more diplomatic message for my new comrade. "Sergeant Bluff wants to know if you would like to work supply with us." I smiled at Arkey, hoping he would not decipher the real meaning behind the dispatch.

"He said that?" Arkey lit a cigarette. "Why didn't he ask me himself?"

I looked away.

"Fick ihn." *Fuck him,* he said, in German, our secret language we spoke to avoid Sergeant Bluff's listening ears. "Okay, I will stay."

"Good," I grinned. "I'll let him know."

"But I don't do this for him. I do this for my friends. I will stay for Dale and Dix." He looked me in the eye. "And you." My cheeks warmed and my chest burned, perhaps from the second-hand smoke, or something else.

Now, standing outside in the cold late autumn evening, I almost believe Arkey and I are the last two people on Earth, in Poland, or at least on this base. Our logistics company is one of the few remaining units. We inherit the garbage, the waste, and the mess the others have left, but also the quiet. The night sky is so clear I see stars, already dead, but born during creation. If I listen closely, I can almost hear the Big Bang.

Not a single sound escapes from the motor pool bay into the atmosphere. Before lights out, my buddies and platoon sergeant always get first dibs on our only latrine. They are men and I am outnumbered, so I go when they are finished. I assume they have disappeared to wash up or have already crawled into their cots. The stillness that remains could almost pass for peace.

A sliver of moonlight falls on Arkey's face as he takes another drag. "Here. I want to give you something," he says, the cigarette perched on his lips.

He untucks the shirttail of his uniform and, in Polish, mumbles to himself. From the front pocket of his trousers, he pulls out a small folding knife and saws at the bottom button of his untucked shirt. With one hand, he folds up the knife, then grips the cigarette. In his other hand, he holds out the button.

"This is a gift for you. From one soldier to another, from a Polish to an American."

Reaching out, I notice my own hands. Dried blood and earth fill the crevices of my broken skin. Embedded under my nails are layers of dirt. The more I wash, the dirtier my hands become. The skin flakes, then cracks open. Grime fills the gaps where my body refuses to knit back together. The filth from Army life infiltrates my bloodstream, becoming a part of me as much as everything else in my past.

When I was a little girl, Mom held me down and scrubbed from my creases and crevices the "rust" of our Kentucky holler. I cried as she pumiced my hands and feet with gritty Lava soap, but for visits with my father in Cincinnati, I had to be spotless. All traces of my hillbilly home had to be removed before my dad would allow me to enter through the front door of his large suburban house.

There, on his front porch, in the bright sunlight, my father stripped me bare. I shivered, putting my hands over the parts I didn't want him to see, but he pulled my arms to my side. It was in the dark places, he said, where things hid. He always found an invisible speck of dirt hiding in a bend of an elbow or between two toes. It was proof of who, what, his daughter was.

· · ·

Tonight, a decade later and an ocean away, I want to hide from Arkey. I fear he will find evidence, like others have, of what I am. The Army forbids me from shoving my hands in my pockets, and I can't conceal my grimy face. In the field, there are few mirrors, so I can only imagine how I look after days, a week, without a shower. I am not here to be pretty, I remind myself. Pretty is a liability.

Still, I consider what I might look like through his eyes. I wonder what he saw that day when he looked up at me while we were stacking boxes on a pallet. He reached out to touch me—another prohibited act while in uniform.

"You have something on your face," he said, wiping my cheekbone.

"That's how it is in the field." My Kevlar bounced on my head as I instinctively pulled away. "I am a soldier."

"But you are a woman." He rested his hand on my cheek.

"No," I readjusted my helmet. Scanning my surroundings for Sergeant Bluff, I prayed that for once I had escaped his notice. "I am a soldier," I repeated.

Between my thumb and forefinger, I roll the olive-green button Arkey has given me, studying it. Like a jeweler appraising a precious gemstone, I hold it up to the moonlight.

Embossed on the surface is an eagle. The plumage of the outstretched wings extends down either side of its body. It spreads its talons, but unlike the American eagle, it holds nothing in its grip. There are no olive branches of peace, but no arrows of war either.

"That is the old Polish eagle. It doesn't have its crown," Arkey says. "These uniforms are from when the Soviet Union still ruled over Poland."

Bringing his boot up to his thigh, he puts his smoke out on the sole. Following military protocol, he fieldstrips the cigarette, pulling the remaining tobacco from the filter, so there's nothing still left smoldering.

"Everything on this Army base is still from the Soviets. Come," he motions for me to step inside the bay doors. He lowers his voice and I wonder if the communists are still listening.

"There," he points across the room to a diagram on the wall. "That tank, you see? It is

Russian." Next to the tank illustration, letters resembling something more like hieroglyphs spell out words I cannot even begin to decipher.

We walk back into the frosty night. "Someone has always tried to rule over us. They think that in my country we are dirty barbarians. They think we are not civilized," he stares down, as if standing over a defeated would-be occupier. "The Polish eagle will have a crown on its head again. No one rules us. Now we are free." He pauses. "Take the button back with you. So you never forget."

From underneath my shirt, I pull out my dog tags. I unsnap the clasp and slide the button down the length of the chain. "There," I say. "It's part of my uniform. I won't forget."

He leans closer. "Can I kiss you?"

My voice cracks and I stutter. "Well, I..."

I do not know how to say it so that he might understand. In the month I have been here, I have forgotten how to speak clean, polite English. I search for the right words, but I am unable to translate. Sergeant Bluff's authority over me has no borders or boundaries. I am a soldier, my NCO reminds me. I am equipment to be used and discarded as he pleases. My pieces and parts are to be inspected for dirt. When my sergeant spies Arkey and me together, his eyes peel away my uniform. I am stripped down to my nakedness. He finds something hiding in the dark places. He will break me down and clean me. I will be fieldstripped like an M-16 rifle.

"You don't want to kiss me?" Arkey asks. "Is it because you are American? Would an American girl never kiss a Polish boy?"

"No. Polish, American, whatever—that doesn't matter," I say. "What matters is that I am a woman."

"You are a soldier." Arkey's vivid green eyes dim to hazel.

I shake my head.

From her throne in the nighttime heavens, the polished moon bathes Arkey and me in a warm glow. Between my breasts rest my cold metal dog tags with the button. Against a backdrop of broken pallets and overflowing garbage we stand alone, together in silence. We stare up at Luna, naked, free, and bright.

Chapter 15

Truthquakes

Sometimes there is little brightness. The night is often naked, raw, and dark, blotted out by tall trees of a dense forest. One has to make time and space to look up at the sky and search for the moon or stars. It doesn't always feel safe to stop and breathe.

During the day, trucks and Humvees drone in the distance. Apache helicopters buzz non-stop overhead. Long stretches of boredom are bookended by periods of everyday Army bullshit like someone yelling for no reason, or assigning us to sweep up clean floors, or ordering us to police up trash where none exists. Moments of terror, although sporadic and brief, come without warning. Those images dot the timeline, and sear into the brain, threatening to blot out all other memories forever after.

In the distance there's a boom, followed by another and another. The ground quakes under my feet. The ground, like my knees, seems to want to buckle. My feet tremble first. The tremors move up my legs and my spine, down my arms and into my hands. At last, my entire body shakes until I'm thrown into a fit of laughter.

"Goddammit," I wheeze through chuckles. "Those motherfucking Apaches are going to kill us if pneumonia doesn't get me first." Arkey slaps me on the back, hard.

"What the hell?" I shrug his hand off my back.

"It will help with your cough," he says.

"Get the fuck off me." I straighten myself up. "I don't need that kind of help then."

Another crash follows as if cued by some Hollywood special effects director. The horizon looks tilted, like the ground has been knocked out of alignment with the sky.

"Your helicopters are blowing holes in my country." He smiles, though his voice is tinged with anger. "First the Russians, now the Americans. Someone is always coming here and trying to destroy my land. Does your Army care what they do to us?"

"No," I shrug. "My Army doesn't care about you." He narrows his eyes. "My Army doesn't care about me either. Look at your boots coming apart at the sole. You get issued one wool parka, and it's filled with holes. Does your Army care about you?"

"That's the Polish Army," his mischievous grin returns as he snickers. "America is different. They give you warm boots and thick coats."

I shake my head. "America isn't that different. We just hide behind some nice uniforms."

My head feels heavy and my ears ring, as if truth could give a person a concussion. I step back and see myself, Arkey, this entire mission from past to present to future. The pieces are all there and I'm starting to put them into place.

"I might die in your country."

An Apache threatens to drown out my words, but not my memory.

CHAPTER 16

HOLDING THE BAG

"We don't need anyone dying in this country," the Lieutenant says to Sergeant Bluff who has lined Dale, Dix, and me up once again in a small formation, as if for inspection. "How would that look if a U.S. soldier gets seriously hurt up here in Poland? That would be a public relations disaster." The L.T. doesn't even try to disguise the anger in his voice. "Is one of your soldiers sick, Sergeant?"

"No, Sir, everyone is fine," Sergeant Bluff says. He raises his eyebrows and attempts a smile, lines forming around his eyes. He shifts from one foot to another and clears his throat.

"What about her?" The L.T. nods his brunette head towards me. His cheeks are a shocking pink as if he has just been slapped by a cold wind or a superior officer. "I heard her coughing earlier. If she needs to go to sick-call—"

"Sir." Sergeant Bluff glances out of the corner of his eye at me. I stand with my eyes wide open as the two men discuss my medical situation. "If I may interrupt. I'm already aware of the situation and it's taken care of." The officer raises an eyebrow. As if pulling a rabbit out of his BDU cap, Sergeant Bluff makes a Ziploc bag of medicine appear. "Sir, as you know we're crunched for time down here at the Class I food distribution point and I don't have a lot of personnel, so they can't be taking time off for sick-call. I noticed she was coughing, so I went to sick-call myself and told the medics I had a sick soldier and got this Cold Pack for her."

Sergeant Bluff dangles the baggie of drugs in front of the Lieutenant. The prescription for a cold has not changed since I had a nasty cough in Basic. Inside the Ziploc is a handful of menthol cough drops collecting at the bottom, a bottle of generic Robitussin laying on its side, threatening to leak out, and a bottle of Army-issued Acetaminophen, aka off-brand Tylenol. I close my eyes and give thanks to whoever was in charge of the universe for this small miracle.

"All right." The Lieutenant glances over at me one last time before turning his attention back to my sergeant. "As long as you're taking care of it."

"Yes, Sir," Sergeant Bluff grins as the L.T. walks out the door behind us. If this were the movies Sergeant Bluff would click his heels together and snap off a salute. Here in the real world, we don't salute indoors and the acting is much more subtle.

As soon as the officer is out of sight, Sergeant Bluff's smile morphs into a scowl. He snorts and mumbles something to himself. He turns, sees us three in formation, and steps back as if startled to see us there. "Dismissed," he says. "Get outside, go find something to do."

"Sergeant," I say with my best mix of Army professionalism and niceness.

"Hmmm." He looks over my head. My heart beats into my throat.

"Um," I stammer. "You mentioned, uh, well, you said, you had a Cold Pack for me, Sergeant?"

Like a dog trying to understand human speech, he cocks his

head to the side. "You trying to take my Cold Pack?" He stares at me as if waiting for an answer. "I can't believe it," he says. "You've got some nerve, Burton, trying to take my Cold Pack. I'm sick and you come asking me for my medicine." He walks off, still holding the bag of medicine.

CHAPTER 17

HOLDING ON

I hold my bladder and my nose as I perform the pee-pee dance with my M-16 in the shit-stained stall where American patriots, secret Polish resistors, and Soviet Communists have all probably let loose their bowels over the last several decades. I'm here now to leave my mark on history and I don't care who sees. I have stopped closing the door. Fuck it. If it doesn't bother half a dozen of my fellow American and Polish soldiers to strip down at the sink, take a shit in the stall, or whip their dicks out in the urinal while I'm in here, then it no longer bothers me either. This place has made me immune to caring about certain things like privacy or nudity or even decency. Such luxuries belong to a person I was in another place.

Now, all I care about is getting my LBE belt unhooked, my trouser belt undone, my BDU fly unbuttoned, my underwear pulled down, and my M-16 stowed so I can position my ass over the porcelain seat before I piss and/or shit myself.

I barely make it before the stream starts flowing. By barely, I mean I don't quite get my britches down before the dam breaks. It looks like the MRE will do its job and keep my bowels stopped up for another day, but piss hits the bowl before my ass touches the seat. A wave of sharp razor blade pain cuts through my bladder at the same moment as relief rushes over me and I yell, "Oh, yeah, Jesus. Fuck me. Goddamn it." My Baptist family would be appalled. Mom would tell me that doesn't sound very ladylike.

None of my family has spent the better part of October at a field site in Poland. Mom certainly has not had to fumble around in her BDU pant pockets for a Maxi pad with an M-16 balanced across her lap long after she has bled through her pad, underwear, and uniform. They will never appreciate that my BDU is designed not only to camouflage the wearer but also to conceal stains from blood and other bodily fluids. Rules of decorum, politeness, and even religious custom are behind me, in a world where people don't worry about survival.

If any of my few dozen Polish soldier brethren walk in to find me howling our heavenly father's name, failing to shut the stall door, that is not my concern. Soldiers don't seem to care that I am often naked in a stall, bathing with a baby wipe as they claim the remaining free stall to destroy. I used to bear the humiliation of walking out, apologizing to Polish soldiers who didn't understand, "I'm so sorry, excuse me," waiting it out in the stall while they finished bathing, pissing, and shitting until they were gone or at least had put their dicks away. But I cannot count the number of times they have failed to sheath their dicks for any task I need to perform in the latrine. In the evenings, I used to fall into my cot after everyone else was asleep because I waited until every man was done shitting, shaving, and showering before I could at last have a turn at the lone sink instead of settling for another baby wipe.

If any of the men in the Polish Army wonder how the latrine sparkles every morning, they haven't let on. I suppose they think there's some magic toilet fairy who comes in every evening to take care of the one urinal that doesn't flush and the toilets that no one bothers to flush. Perhaps they think Americans are rich enough to travel with some latrine priest who performs exorcism rituals, banishing demons from that bathroom overnight. They must know it's me, though, because once they saw me with the scrub brush Sergeant Bluff said now belongs to me through the duration of our mission. Like my American comrades, they must not care that a fellow soldier, one soldier, must take an hour out of her personal time to clean up after an entire company of men. Perhaps they don't see me as a soldier.

My platoon sergeant doesn't see me as a soldier. He doesn't see me as a person. He sees me only as that dirty word in the Army, a female, a liability. I'm caught in a game with rules in place to ensure I will lose, yet I cannot afford to lose. We stare each other down, knowing but refusing to acknowledge how the other is playing. I know he's cheating, changing the rules, but he created the game, so there's nothing I can do about it but keep up. I maintain my poker face, pretend to be ignorant, all the while looking for patterns, a method that I can exploit. I refuse to believe in the complete randomness of the universe or Sergeant Bluff's mindfucks.

I know I'm finished when I can no longer hold my breath. Not only is that how I know it's time for me to yank up my pants and button them up outside, but that's how I know I'm done cleaning the shithole that passes as our latrine. Now that I have run out of Poland's National Brand bathroom cleaner and bleach I wipe the sink down with paper towels and clean the toilets with water from their bowls. The self-draining urinal gets an occasional swipe with the brush, but otherwise it has survived decades without human intervention, and I figure it can survive one more month. If Sergeant Bluff complains, I can complain again about his lack of cooperation in obtaining the necessary cleaning supplies or just blame it on the guys destroying the place. This game is called, "There. I technically cleaned the latrines."

Maybe Sergeant Bluff thinks the only time a woman is supposed to be in the latrine is when she is cleaning it.

Today at the Class I point he says, "You're taking too much time to use the latrine. I've been watching you and you're just slacking. You go twice as much as Dix or Dale and then you take at least fifteen minutes every time."

I open my mouth to argue that those fifteen minutes include the trek across rugged terrain with a bad ankle, the time it takes to undo all my clothes once I'm in the stall, and—because I'm on my period—changing my pad. Then I think better of it, supposing my defense will also be my confession. I will be admitting that I'm a woman and I'm frail, that I need special accommodations to do the same job as men. It will serve as proof, the proof that Sergeant Bluff is looking for to convict me and all females of being women and unfit for service.

"From now on," he says, "if you can get to the latrine and back in the amount of time that it takes these guys to smoke a cigarette, then you can go. Let me catch you trying to get out of doing your job again by abusing latrine privileges and I'll have you pulling extra duty."

When he is out of earshot, I spit, "I'm already doing extra duty, cleaning every Army's piss and shit in Poland." Not using the latrine until the end of the day is an impossibility under these rules. My only option is to stop drinking water.

Vibrant orange leaves stand in stark contrast to the low gray Polish skies. The cool, clear, cloudless days of late summer are gone. Overnight the seasons have shifted, and I wake up to a cold autumn frost and a bladder that will no longer cooperate. The change in my mood is as obvious as the change in the weather. After pushing through a throng of Polish men to use the latrine, but not before dribbling on myself, I make my way to the Class I Point.

"I'm done with Sergeant Bluff's shit," I say to my buddies as I wrap myself inside my Gore-Tex jacket and massage my sinus passages. My head is ready to explode and I sound as if I am talking through my left nostril. "I don't feel like playing his little reindeer games today."

Through the smoke of their second cigarettes of the morning, Dale and Dix peer at me. I contemplate confessing everything from the walking pneumonia, the stiff ankle, my throbbing sinuses, even the so-called female issues of incontinence and menstruation. Some sort of pride, not shyness, holds me back. I can't bring myself to admit to my comrades my weaknesses.

"I need to use the latrine today." I study their faces as they exchange concerned looks.

My self-conscious paranoia kicks in. I wonder if they know. I wonder if Sergeant Bluff knows. How could they not know when I am so aware of everything my body is doing? I wonder if they know when I feel the gush of blood into my underwear or how my bottom stings from my sweat mixing with the stale blood collecting on a thin pad asked to work twelve hours. My camo BDUs hide the blood. Maybe the uniform was designed for the camouflaging of a soldier's blood to spare comrades from the ugly truth of trading one's life to the Army.

Never before has peeing or getting my period been a problem in the Army, but Sergeant Bluff has created a problem where there isn't one, and now it's my job to find the solution.

Today I declare to my buddies, "I'm sick of Sergeant Bluff's game to set me up for failure. I refuse to hold my piss all day from zero dark thirty until twenty dark thirty."

Staring at Dale puffing on his cigarette, I tell them to smoke a little slower while I hit the latrine. They say they'll do one better and smoke two cigarettes while I'm gone. Together the three of us find loopholes in Sergeant Bluff's order. It's a win-win. I double-time it to the toilet as my buddies light up cigarettes, taking slow drags and practicing smoke rings. As one light goes out, they fire another one up.

Chapter 18

Nightmares and Realities

"They're firing on us." I can't tell if I actually spoke the words or if I only saw them written across my dreaming brain.

The clang of metal-on-metal ringing through the night jerks me from my sleep. Beneath my body, my cot quivers. Reaching out of my Gore-Tex modular sleeping bag, instinctively I grope for my M-16. I sleep with my weapon stretched alongside my body. Throughout the night, half asleep, I rub my hand along the length of its icy barrel to reassure myself that it is still there, protecting me. "Love your rifle," drill sergeants said. "Love it more than your mommy, your wife, even your children." I didn't always under-stand what that meant, but I'm learning.

"Gas, gas, gas," I mumble, shaking off sleep. "We've been hit." Somewhere deep inside my inner ear my body recalls the noise. The dinging sound of metal piercing the silent night air is an alert for a gas attack. I fumble for my gas mask, where I hope I've had the good sense to put it within arms-reach. I wait for the familiar clouds and odor of CS to fill the darkness. When fumes fail to materialize and I cannot locate my mask, I at last have a vague understanding that this is not Basic Training circa 1997. When the butt of my M-16 wedges itself into my lower abdomen I can no longer pretend this is some fever dream. I'm in a nightmare reality, a war created by Sergeant Bluff.

My chest tightens, and I wheeze. I swear I can feel, even taste, the lingering effects of tear gas. Beads of sweat form on my forehead and sweat drips down my spine. In the crisp, chilly air, I shiver. My orientation in time and place has not made it through the fogginess of my brain. I widen my eyes. to gage my surroundings. A small beam of silver moonlight shines through some high, distant windows off to my right.

I look towards the end of my cot into blackness, recalling only what my body recorded moments earlier. A clanging started at the foot of my cot, sending tremors rippling through my feet, legs, and up my spine into my head. No. It was not an alarm for gas. At the foot of my cot hovers a shadow, a phantom. I hear his heart beating, I feel his breath. I don't move a muscle, I don't blink.

I'm transported to a time when as a young girl I woke to ghostly figures at midnight in my bedroom at Mamaw's little white, clapboard house on the farm. The shadows cast by the moonlight and the calls of the whippoorwills somehow transformed into silvery aliens and dark demons whispering and hovering at the foot of my bed. I pulled the covers tight, trembled, and gasped for air. Sleeping beside me in a shared bed at Mamaw's was my little brother. I shook him to tell him someone was in the room. Annoyed, he told me to leave him alone. He said I was older than him but acting like a big dumb baby scared of the dark. I told myself to be the older sister, the brave girl who knew this was just my overactive imagination.

. . .

Just my imagination. On my cot in Poland I tell myself that's all this is too. I'm back in Basic on a field training exercise that time the drill sergeants gassed us in the night. Or I'm a little kid again, who can't sleep after watching too many *Twilight Zone* episodes. I am anywhere but here, in a motor pool bay in Poland, and this is not happening. But here and now, reality creeps in.

Frozen somewhere among real life, memories, and night terrors, I wait. I wait with my hand on my M-16. With a slow and controlled motion, I pull my feet back. I try not to rustle the sleeping bag or bring attention to myself as I bend my knees towards my hips. My eyes have not adjusted to being awake. I can't see what might see me.

To my left I hear a loud snore, a grunt, then a cough. A cot squeaks as a weight I recognize comes down hard on it. "Dale," I look over and whisper, finally working up the nerve to move, to speak. After our many trips to the field together, my buddy's sighs, his huffs, all his nonverbal utterances are as familiar to me as his voice. On the other side of Dale someone snores, then farts. It is Dix, I recognize his sounds, too. At last it occurs to me where I am. I am with my buddies, and we're in Poland. Dale grunts again. I consider reaching over and nudging him with my rifle. On this mock deployment, we carry no ammo, so I'm not afraid of a friendly fire incident. However, I'm gripped by a greater fear, the fear that Dale would tell me I was just being stupid, that this was all in my head.

Sitting in the dark, I am alone in my horror. I listen for the faintest sounds of life coming from the end of my cot. The motor pool bay goes silent and I hold my breath. There is a vortex, an empty spot where something once was. I don't dare believe the phantom is gone, so I remain still but ready with my rifle.

At last, from far across the bay, beyond Dale and Dix, where Sergeant Bluff sleeps, boots shuffle across the floor, a cot whines, and someone moans out his fatigue and exasperation. There's the sound of canvas squeaking as it stretches under a body, the teeth of a zipper as someone closes himself inside a sleeping bag, and the thump of an M-16 coming to rest on the concrete floor. Only when I hear snoring from that side of the motor pool do I exhale. I lay down on my cot and wriggle into my sleeping bag. I pull my M-16 onto my chest and hug it as I stare up at the rafters. Whether the danger in the night is real or a nightmare, I can't be sure. Just to be safe, I vow to never close my eyes again just in case at night the devil stalks.

Chapter 19

The Devil Went Up to Poland

The devil's got into Sergeant Bluff. That's what the old folks up the hollers would've said. Now people might say he's gone mad. I laugh about it, literally laugh out loud, how everyone thought I'd snap. Mom said I wasn't strong enough to handle the pressures of life, especially not the military life. My comrades in the warehouse said they were taking bets on when I'd go postal because I'm weak. It isn't me who has cracked into tiny pieces like Humpty Dumpty. It isn't even Dix or Dale. It is our platoon leader.

Poland feels like a long, dark night. Tonight, during the never-ending dark night, I've lost track of time again. I'm late. We all are. Dale, Dix and me. Sergeant Bluff denied requests to both go to chow and the showers. We argued it was ridiculous to not allow us to eat and shower when there was no more work that evening. Sergeant Bluff told us we had an hour until lights out, to choose one or the other.

We all understood he was using his authority for no other reason to torture us. I wondered if it was all a sick game in the name of training to starve us, keep us cold and dirty, to deny us medicine and to lurk over us at night, but I feared Sergeant Bluff had gone too deep. He had lost sense of what was real and what was a game. At first I trusted he would not do anything to hurt us, that he had it under control, but I no longer believe that. I fear I won't come back from Poland.

Dale, Dix, and I chose to go to both chow and the showers. The decision was a bit of "Yeah, fuck you Sergeant Bluff," but also part of "Well, if we are going to die, at least we will have died clean with full bellies."

As soon as we returned from the motor pool, my buddies stayed outside and smoked while I ran inside to hang up my damp towel and put away my shaving kit of toiletries. After I finish in the small room where we keep our rucksacks, I look for my buddies, who must be finished with their smoke break. On the other side of the motor pool, where the Polish soldiers sleep, I peek my head in, looking to see if they're hanging out with Arkey. Half the lights are turned out and the cots are empty. My buddies are not there.

I walk down the small corridor that divides the two halves of the motor pool toward our bay. The quiet forms a vacuum inside my ear canals. I listen, but there is silence. I feel the absence of my two friends. A coldness creeps from the tips of my fingers and all the way through the rest of my body. I need to find Dale and Dix. Something is off and I am worried about them. My feet are glued to the floor. I want nothing less than to throw myself into some horrible fate to which I am certain my buddies have succumbed. The blood pumping through my ears becomes louder, but I take a deep breath and take a step forward.

As I emerge from the narrow hallway into the vast open bay, Sergeant Bluff's voice greets me as an echo. It is bouncing off the rafters, from the cinder block walls to the concrete floor. I crane my head to locate the source of the sound. Dix's back confronts me as he stands watching the horror unfold. Facing Sergeant Bluff, Dale stands as if at attention with his M-16 slung over his shoulder, light glancing off the sharp edges of his left side of his profile. Our platoon leader bounces from foot to foot, barking, laughing. His eyes are wide and spit hangs from his jowls, like a pit-bull in a fighting ring. I've never seen him like this. I have never seen any sergeant so undisciplined, so unprofessional.

Holding my breath, I set my rucksack down and tiptoe to Dix's side. "What the fuck is going on?"

He jumps back as if startled to find I've materialized from the ether. "Shh," he giggles like a kid spying on some adult conversation. "Sergeant Bluff is giving Dale an ass chewing."

"Yeah, but..." I can't seem to make sense of the odd scene. "Is this about us being late?"

Dix gives no answer. He smiles and stares as if in some trance.

I stand on the sidelines, my brain failing me. I register movement and sound, but not their meanings. My frontal lobe is unable to process language, my amygdala fails to read gestures or facial expressions. I'm little more than a network of nerves connected to sense organs. I don't know what I've walked in on.

I consider bolting and hiding before our NCO can turn his wrath on me. This might be some unresolved issue between Dale and Sergeant Bluff, and I wonder if I should run before I get sucked into it. But I don't. Whatever this is, it is better if my buddies and I face it all together.

Sergeant Bluff punches two fists into the air on either side of his head. Dale jerks back. I gasp, jumping backwards, pulling Dix by the sleeve along with me.

"Is everyone high?" I ask. "What the hell is going on?"

Sergeant Bluff notices us, apparently for the first time. He turns his attention back to Dale. "I don't know who the fuck you think you are dealing with." He moves in closer, nose to nose. "You're nobody, you and your friends, you're nothing. But you know who I am? I am the Army."

Dale's hair, having grown shaggy during our time here, is

drenched in sweat despite the cold. His face flushes across his cheeks as if fevered. His hazel eyes are wide black disks. I know this look. I feel it sometimes on my own face when I let my mind float away while my body stays to take the punishment.

With the slight movement of his left hand, he reaches for the black webbed strap of his M-16 on the front of the same shoulder. He pulls down on it and the rifle creeps up his back. He gives the strap some slack, letting the weapon fall. He repeats the process again and again, the movement so slight that I wonder if it is detectable to anyone, even him.

Sergeant Bluff's eyes zero in on Dale's hand. He cocks his head to one side, "You want to hit me?" He grins wide like he's hoping for an affirmative answer. "Hmm? Is that what you want to do? I see you grabbing at your gun, boy."

I don't trust my senses. I wonder if it is possible that our platoon sergeant not only called another soldier a boy and a M-16 a gun instead of a rifle or weapon, but also asked his soldier to hit him.

Dale gropes at the weapon again, his chest rising and falling. His brows twitch, but his eyes have a vacant, faraway stare. Sergeant Bluff drops to his knees and links his fingers, as if in prayer, and stares up at Dale. "Please." He shakes his clasped hands up at our friend. "I'm begging you. I want you to. Do it. Hit me, please."

Fire burns behind Dale's eyes. Muscles and tendons in his jaw flex as he stares down at Sergeant Bluff mocking and pleading. He yanks down on the strap, slamming the rifle into the back of his shoulder. With his right hand he reaches across his chest to put his other hand on the webbing.

"Dale," my voice rings through the bay. Both he and Sergeant Bluff face me. "Don't do it. You don't want to spend the rest of your life busting blocks in Leavenworth for him."

"Let him hit me if he wants to hit me," Sergeant Bluff grins.

Dale looks down at the floor with his mouth open, swaying back and forth.

"Dale," I say in a soft voice. And just like I was trained in Basic to speak to a soldier suffering from shock, I reassure the casualty, say whatever they need to hear. "Everything's going to be okay. We're getting ready to leave for chow and then we're going to head to the shower point after." His eyes flicker with signs of life, but his eyelids close and I'm afraid I'll lose him again. "Dale," I say again, louder as if issuing an order. He snaps awake and looks at me. "Come over here with us."

CHAPTER 20

LITTLE RUNAWAY

"Why are you up here with us?" Specialist Roberts asks Dale and me. Just inside the front gate, he and PFC Perez pull night guard under a single light mounted to what looks like a telephone pole.

"Because Sergeant Bluff told us to pull your guard duty," Dale says.

Perez sits shivering inside her field jacket with her M-16 beside her. The sky is a flawless black onyx with white pinpoints of light serving as stars. In a moment meant to be a punishment, I take time to check out, look up, breathe. I come back to Earth when I notice my breath condensing in the cold air. In an attempt to keep my body temperature up, I bounce on my toes. If Sergeant Bluff were here, he would reprimand me for behaving more like a child than a disciplined soldier.

"You're sure? That's what he said?" Roberts looks at Dale then me.

"Yep," Dale says and I nod in agreement. "Me, Burton, and Dix are pulling guard duty for your platoon tonight."

Perez shakes her head. "Nope. I didn't hear nothing about this." With her arms folded, she sits with her chin tucked and her legs out in front of her. "The first general order is 'I will guard everything within the limits of my post and—'"

"Quit my post only when properly relieved," I laugh. "Yes, we all know our general orders. Did you just graduate Basic or something? Listen, you're being relieved. We're here. You can go."

"It says *properly* relieved." She looks up at me from under her Kevlar.

"Jesus." I rock back and forth on my heels. "It makes no difference to me if y'all want to freeze your asses off here all night with us, but we've got to be out here. Those are our orders."

Roberts looks back at Perez, who refuses to budge, then back at Dale and me, who are in the process of finding additional seating. "Alright," he says. "Let me run and find our platoon sergeant and ask him what's going on. As long as there's someone up here it will be okay."

Roberts disappears into the night only to return several minutes later. He catches his breath from running in full battle rattle and says, "I talked to our sergeant. He said he didn't know anything about it, but if you all want to give us a night off, that's fine by him as long as someone's guarding the gate."

"Seriously?" Perez asks.

"Told you." I move over behind her chair. "Up, up, up, get up. Go to bed."

"Hell, yeah." She grabs her rifle.

Roberts is still shaking his head. "I don't understand. The three of you going to pull guard duty all night? Why would Sergeant Bluff want you all to do that?"

"Because we're bad, bad soldiers and we need to be punished." I push my Kevlar up with the tip of my M-16.

Perez and Roberts look at each other, then howl with laughter. "Oh, my God, Burton." Roberts grabs his ribs through his Gore-Tex coat. "You're hilarious. Bad, bad soldiers. Whew." Dale and I shrug at one another.

"Yep," I say. "That's me. I'm full of jokes. So is Sergeant Bluff. Like this one he's playing on us tonight. You all should come over to the Class I point sometime and see the jokes we all got. This whole mission has been *so* fun. Oh, my God. It's a regular vacation on the Army's dime to Poland."

"If I weren't so tired," Perez says, laughing and shaking her head, "I'd seriously stay up here and just listen to you talk. This shit is hilarious."

"Yeah, gather 'round y'all, and let ole Burton tell you a story, a cautionary tale about the Army. Bring your friends, bring your young'uns and sit them around me and I'll tell them about an old soldier and her comrades who survived the brutal NATO Mission to Poland."

Dale widens his eyes and looks at me like I've lost my mind. I burst out laughing.

"Damn." Roberts shakes his head as he walks off. "I never knew you were so funny. 'Bad, bad soldiers...'"

Dale and I fill the seats of Perez and Roberts, the seats still warm from their body heat. Dale sits upright with his hands shoved between his thighs. I slouch as Perez did with my arms crossed over my body, but I hug my legs close to me to trap as much body heat as possible. No one will come through the gate all night. Already, despite the cold, I feel myself fighting sleep. Guard change occurs every hour. However, since there are only three of us, one of us will always pull two consecutive hours while the other soldier leaves to go wake up the third.

Dale has volunteered to pull the first two hours. After my first hour I will go wake up Dix, who will work with Dale during his second hour. Dale will come wake me up, so Dix and I can work together. I will pull my second of two consecutive hours with Dale, then I will go wake up Dix again. So it will go all night until Sergeant Bluff wakes up in the morning and decides we are finished and can go to work in the Class I point.

"You were funny," Dale says. "What's got into you?"

"Ain't I always funny?" I smile.

"Yeah," he shrugs. "I guess. Back in Germany. Just not up here."

"It wasn't that funny, really. I was just telling the truth."

"Yeah, it's definitely the truth." He blows on his hands and rubs them together. "They do seem a little drunk. Slaphappy, I guess. Seems like everyone's going crazy up here. But they think you're really joking. I don't think they know that Sergeant Bluff really is punishing us when all we really did was go to chow and shower. Everyone in the other platoons seems to be enjoying it up here, like it's some vacation."

"I know, right," I laugh. "A lot of them even got to go on the field trip into town with the Chaplain. That day he came to see how we were settling in right after we got here, Sergeant Bluff said, 'If my soldiers need you they can ask for you.' Jesus. Like he'd ever let us see the Chaplain. He won't even let us get a fucking cough drop from sick-call."

"And now this bullshit. He consistently sets us up for failure. After letting us have only one MRE a day and almost starving us to death, he finally lets us go to chow—but just to punish us. This, this right here is what he wanted," Dale says, standing up. With his back to me, he paces. He balls his fists and punches toward the ground. "God. Fuck the Army. FTA, man. FTA. He waits for us to fuck up or he pushes us so he can have real evidence of why he punished us."

"Yeah, I know," I say. "Remember how they hauled my ass down to the MP station for hitting that truck with the forklift when they ordered me to get on it with no license? Sergeant Bluff and Sergeant Bennett threatened to kick me out over that shit. They wanted to send me home with a dishonorable discharge over an accident and their own failed leadership. I won't let them turn me into the Shitbag they claim I am."

"Jesus, he really wants to see how much we can take before we snap."

"He wants to see how much we can take before we die." I stare at the back of Dale's brain bucket.

He sits back down with a heavy sigh. "We just have to keep playing his game. It's all we can do if we want to survive."

"I'm tired of trying to figure out how to survive."

I look past my left shoulder. The gate reminds me less of a military gate and more of the entrance to some fairgrounds. If it weren't for the concertina wire surrounding the entire base and the missing turnstiles, this place would look like the overgrown site of a forgotten carnival.

"What do you think is outside the gate?" I look over at my friend. "Some of the guys in the water platoon said a line of taxis is just sitting right out front. Why would there be taxis, do you think? Are there a bunch of rich asshole NATO officers taking cabs to bars and shit in the evening while the rest of us dumb fucks are out here playing war?"

He chuckles and shrugs, "Probably wishful thinking." He stomps his feet on the ground. I feel my own toes going numb and wiggle them inside my boots. "There's a city not far from here, you know. That's where the Chaplain took the other soldiers on that trip. The taxis are probably hoping that a few of us will sneak off base and go to town."

"Maybe they think some of us will finally break and go AWOL," I say, standing up and walking closer to the gate for a better look. "I know a guy back in the States who went AWOL."

"Yeah," Dale says.

"A big, loudmouth infantryman who was always calling me a pussy and the supply people poges. He ran off from his base at Fort Campbell, back to his mommy in our hometown in the Eastern part of the state."

"Figures." Dale makes a raspberry sound. "I hope the MPs gave him an ass-beating when they caught him. Did they?"

"I wish, but no. He had his mommy call his Colonel and get him a new assignment."

"Infantrymen are always running their mouths about how tough they are and how supply just sits in some cozy office. No one knows the shit we all put up with." Dale closes his eyes and huffs. "So nothing happened to that guy?"

"Nope.

"How do you know all this for sure? Did you go to high school with him?"

"Yeah, you could say that. I know his family really well."

I don't tell my buddy I know because this guy is my family, my own brother.

When I get Dix up for his hour of duty, I almost hate to wake him since I know that first hour is the deepest, most sound sleep a soldier will get. That initial sixty minutes feel the safest, like the bogeyman won't come for you until later when he thinks you and your comrades are completely out. But when he rolls over and mumbles something that sounds like a mix between "fuck off" and "go away", I give him a hard shove.

"Get your ass up. You've got guard duty, asshole," I say.

He doesn't speak a word or open his eyes. Instead, like a robot programmed to respond to orders given in such a manner, he sits up in his cot, slings his feet to the side, and puts his boots on.

After Dix is gone, I head to the latrine with my rucksack, then to the storage room where we keep duffel bags and other personal items. I ease the door shut, then flip on the light. I rummage through our stash of food. I always keep a banana-nut muffin on my person, but I steal a few more. I listen at the door for Sergeant Bluff, and when I'm sure he's not coming I dig through my duffel. I find the t-shirt, a fitted silver Fishbone brand hoodie, some coordinating gray corduroys, and the Adidas shelltoes I brought with me. I ensure that in my wallet I have German Deutschmarks, Polish Złoty, American Dollars, and credit cards. I toss the clothes and food along with my passport into my ruck.

Looking at the passport, I laugh. At the urging of Sergeant Bluff, who said if we were separated from our group we might get detained at the border, I went to the Munich consulate a month or so before we left and got my first passport. My fellow soldiers were pissed because I got off work to drive to Munich despite how busy we were prepping for Victory Strike. I was surprised he let me have the day off, since he claimed we didn't even have a few hours to spare in order to cast our absentee ballots to decide if either Bush or Gore would be our next Commander-in-Chief. He framed getting a passport, however, as just good sense. I saw it as a sign. Tonight I see it as an opportunity.

I creep back into my cot and throw my ruck down on the floor beside me. I lie on top of my sleeping bag in my full uniform and boots, staring up at the ceiling. When Dale comes to tell me it is my turn for guard duty, I haven't slept a wink.

Wearing my Kevlar, my LBE, and carrying my ruck and M-16, I make my way to the main gate. Dix, sitting in the same chair I occupied an hour ago, raises an eyebrow.

"Damn, Burton," he says as I throw my ruck down in front of Dale's former chair. "You marching off to battle? Why'd you bring your ruck?"

"Oh," I say. "I've got two hours up here. I want to be prepared, so I brought snacks and stuff. I got my gloves in there. I'm not like you guys, trying to look tough without gloves. That's why I wore my cold weather boots, too, see?" I pick up a foot and show off my heavy boots with the cotton-like stuffing in the toe. "I have a book in there too to help me stay awake. No one's going to come by and see me reading. Besides," I give the rucksack a swift kick with the toe of my boot. "Fuck them. I'm about done with stupid shit at this point."

He nods. "Yeah, Dale and I decided to take turns keeping watch so the other one can sleep up here. We can't stay awake, so..." His chin falls to his chest.

"You want to go first?" I ask.

"Okay," he closes his eyes.

I find my gloves in my ruck and feel the rest of the items to make sure they're real. Then I close it up tight and squeeze it with my feet back towards my chair. My breath vaporizes and threatens to crystalize in the dim amber light shining from overhead. I search the cloudless sky for the Milky Way, hoping for something exciting like comets. There are a few bright twinkling stars, some may belong to constellations, and others may be planets. One is so bright I think it must be a Christmas star, but it's only October. It could be Christmas Eve, for all I know. I've lost track of how long I've been here. Tonight has the feeling of anticipation and snow in the air.

I stare at the gate, then down at my watch while Dix dozes. It is so still on base and my thoughts are so loud, I worry if everyone else can hear what I'm thinking. I try to quiet my mind, but I can't. Leaving and how I'll do it occupy my brain.

When Dix goes to wake up Dale, that's when I'll do it. I'll fling down my rifle, throw off my battle rattle, and I'll run. I'll run as fast as I can with my bronchitis and bad ankle straight out the gate. I'll hail a cab to the nearest train station, where I'll go to the airport. I'll fly to the States, but I won't go home because home won't understand. I'll go to California, to Berkeley, where I always dreamed of going someday. They'll listen to me there. I'll check myself into a civilian hospital because I'm sick, I'm really sick. From my hospital bed, I'll pen an Op Ed and send it to every newspaper I can think of. I'll tell it all, about how our sergeant has brought us here to starve us, deprive us of food, showers, even latrines and medical treatment. I'll say how at first it was supposed to be some sick game of Sergeant Bluff's, where he would teach us "spoiled little brats" what real deployments are like, but now he's gone too far. He's slipped out of reality into this make-believe world of his. Now we are fighting to stay alive. I will tell it all. People will see what he's doing to my buddies.

I imagine living in some artist's shack in SoCal or even Tijuana, churning out cheap paintings or subversive writings. Going AWOL, speaking out against the Army, would make me a pariah. I would lose all the benefits I would have been entitled to as a veteran. Some people, like my family, would hate me forever. I would never be able to face them or those in my hometown again. If I did this, I would have to live in poverty, thanks to my bad discharge. I couldn't even get student loans to go back to college if I wanted to. There would be no going back once I made this decision.

I am not sure if I can do this, but if I am going to live, I have to. I don't need as much as I thought I did to be happy. Being here has taught me that. I don't need a car or a fancy place to live or even a lot of money. As long as I have enough to eat I will be okay. My family is of little support to me and I came here to escape them, anyway. In many ways my buddies are more like my family than the one I was born into. With a few close friends on the outside, I know I could make it. All I want is to be healthy and never have to sleep with my eyes open again.

"Get up," I elbow Dix, "Time to go wake up Dale." Again he stands up without speaking, a body obeying orders. He picks up his rifle and heads in the direction of the Class I point, in the opposite direction of the gate. It will be at least ten or fifteen minutes before Dale arrives for his shift.

I watch Dix disappear into the blackness of the night. I get up and stretch. I look in the direction of the gate, hoping to see head-lights, taillights, city lights. There is nothing. The tales of taxis might be soldier's tales. I pick up my rucksack and put it in my chair. Still, though, I could ruck into the village until I found a phone. I could take back roads, dirt roads, side roads into forests and never be found. Not only am I a soldier, but I've been navigating woods and hills since I was in kindergarten. If I had to swim across the Atlantic to escape, I bet I could do it.

I sling the rucksack on my back and walk around in circles. My eyes dart back and forth between the gate and the direction where I anticipate Dale. Walking toward the gate, still wearing all my gear and carrying my M-16, I stop and look back at the two empty seats my buddies will occupy once I am gone. I walk back to the chairs and put down my rifle. My hands shake, but I feel immune to the cold. Again, I start toward the gate.

Halfway between the gate and our guard post my feet feel frozen to the ground. I grab my throat. It's so sore and tight, I can't breathe. I scratch at invisible worms and bugs crawling on my face and neck. I think I might vomit and lose my bowels at the same time. I wonder if I've developed some sudden allergic reaction to this place, like a kid who can't go into the elephant tent at the circus because of a peanut allergy.

I throw off my ruck and kick it. I want to cry, but I'm all dried up. There's no escape. Even if I wrote my story, no one would believe me. No one so far has believed me or anyone else who has spoken up. Just like my Shitbag status now discredits me, so too would my status as a deserter. There is little empathy for anyone, especially a woman who runs away from the Army.

When I found out my brother had run off from Ft. Campbell, in my head I could hear his name–my name–disgraced as his fellow soldiers said, "Burton has gone AWOL. That fucking Shitbag." When Mom told me, I felt the breath knocked out of me. I wanted to vomit or cry, or both. Instead I was silent, in shock.

Nothing, I believed, justified leaving behind one's comrades and running home to Mommy, especially when a person brags about his willingness, even eagerness, to take a bullet for their country. How can we call ourselves soldiers when faced with the reality of our own deaths, we run away?

Now, however, I can understand the agony, even fear, my brother must have felt to make him commit such a drastic act. As I contemplate going AWOL to save myself from a slow and agonizing death at the hands of my sergeant, I justify it by saying I no longer have an allegiance to an Army who has turned a blind eye to what this man has done. I say it is not that I am scared of dying in battle, but that I see no use in dying for a madman's sick pleasure. I tell myself I am not really leaving my buddies, but that once I am safe and well, in a sense, I will come back for them. I will write the truth. And the truth will save them.

The truth is I will have left my friends behind in the middle of B.F.E with Sergeant Bluff as I head for safety on the United States West Coast.

I can't do it. I can't leave.

CHAPTER 21

THE LABYRINTH

"Leave. Go on. Right now," Sergeant Bluff barks over my left shoulder to Dale and Dix. "Leave her."

Despite my insulated boots, the cold from the concrete floors of the motor pool bay makes the nerves in my toes hum. I recognize the darkness that's descending just outside the bay doors behind my back by the blanket of brisk air it drapes over my shoulders.

In a world without clocks or even calendars, I tell time through the natural rhythm of day and night, month and year. It's not eighteen hundred hours or even six o'clock at night civilian time, it's that time of day in late fall in Eastern Europe when the sun has gone down and shades of purple, navy blue, and inky black have replaced muted greens, browns, and oranges.

Dale and Dix raise their eyebrows. They shift their weight from one foot to the other. They dart their eyes back and forth between each other. I feel their eyes on me, waiting for my response. I sense their response as I see it in my peripheral vision. I've developed eyes in the back of my head and a sixth sense for anticipating actions and reactions.

"Leave her. You heard me. Go on to chow without her. There's no reason you three need to be together all the time." Sergeant Bluff doesn't stop for a breath. "And if you see your little Polack buddy, you tell him he can get his gear and go back to his unit. We're done with him." Dale and Dix hesitate. I can almost hear them holding their breath. "I'm giving you an hour and you'd better not be late." Still my buddies do not move. Sergeant Bluff's voice reveals his impatience. "What are you waiting on? Her? I wear the rank. I gave you an order."

Dale and Dix's boots shuffle all warmth out the door with them. A freezing cold quiet creeps into the motor pool. The room takes on a hazy glow and the floor threatens to swallow me up. I feel like I've fallen through the looking glass.

Sergeant Bluff stands inches from my face. He steps in closer, staring into my wide blue eyes. Then he jerks his neck and recoils, looking me from head to toe as if trying to determine where the stench is coming from. Curling one side of his lip and scrunching his nose, he shakes his head and snorts. My cheeks flush and my eyes water. I can't tell if I'm about to sneeze or shout, cough or cry.

"C'mon, Burton. Leave your M-16 over with mine by my cot." His voice is tired, like this NATO mission has been one big test to see if I'm cut out to be a soldier and I've failed. "We're leaving soon. We need to get these boxes onto as few pallets as possible so we can send them out of here." He walks and talks as I follow. We make our way into rows of pallets with cardboard boxes of food stacked taller than us. A few weeks ago the sight of so much verboten food would have overwhelmed my operating system. Now, like my nagging pain and burning questions, hunger runs in the background of my brain.

"Yes, Sergeant," I say. "Where do you want me to start?"

Without word or sound he disappears behind a towering skyscraper of boxes. The deafening silence is interrupted only by the buzzing of the canister lights overhead. I tiptoe further into the stacks where all the fluorescent light has been gobbled up. The cardboard maze twists and turns like some warehouse version of the labyrinths in the castle gardens back in Germany. I contemplate throwing crumbs of the leftover Otis Spunkmeyer muffin in my BDU pocket onto the floor so I can find my way back out.

Before rounding each bend, I stop and peer around the corner. I walk down row after row in search of my platoon sergeant, but come up empty each time. At last I come to a row of boxes blocking me in. Reaching the end, I turn around and try to feel my way out. I turn a corner but end up at a dead end, so I retrace my steps and try again. As I round the bend, Sergeant Bluff looms large, blocking my exit. Smiling down at me, he spreads his body out to take up the whole aisle. "Oh!" Startled, I jump back. He laughs, putting his hands on his hips. I try to pass him on his right and he steps in front of me. When I move to his left, he again steps in front of me. He grins down at me as we do this dance a couple of more times. Without my M-16 all I have is a Gerber knife on the left hip of my belt. My hands shaking, I reach to unbuckle my knife. Sergeant Bluff's eyes follow my left hand. He laughs, as if amused. I drop my hand, then without a word, he steps aside and I slide past him.

I find my way to the back end of the row, only to be blocked in by pallets half-filled with boxes. I can see the back doors of the bay, but I cannot escape. My heart pounds its way into my throat, but I have to keep my bearings. To my left, over a stack of boxes about chest-high, I can see an aisle that might lead me toward the front of the bay. From there I could grab my weapon from where I left it. The best way out is to cut a new path. Tossing the boxes onto the pallet, I clear my way out. I pick up some speed as I head straight down the path, but as soon as I turn another corner, from behind me I hear the thud of boots landing on concrete. I pivot just in time to see him lunge out from behind a pile of boxes.

"Aaagh," he growls and stretches his arms out and overhead like the bad guy in a slasher film. I gasp and almost fall backwards. As if some wizard has cast a spell on us, we are both frozen, staring, not even blinking. My feet are glued to the ground and my face feels contorted into a look of horror. Sergeant Bluff leans forward on his toes, almost levitating, as his hands reach toward me. Then just as suddenly as the spell was cast, it is broken. He lowers himself down to his heels and slaps his hands to his sides. His laughter rings through the bay.

I do an about face and as if guided by an invisible compass, in a matter of seconds I find my way out of the labyrinth and back to my M-16. I pick it up and head back to my cot to find the rest of my gear. I steady my hands in order to zip up my Gore-Tex jacket and buckle my ammo belt. I glance at my watch, but my mind doesn't make sense of the time. Someone should be looking for me as I am sure I was gone hours, days, even. But the hands of my watch have hardly moved.

I pick up my Kevlar helmet and put it on my head, ready for what may come next.

"Chowtime, Burton," a voice from inside the labyrinth calls out. "You can go now."

To enter the maze of the Polish forest at night is to pass through a black hole. The towering, centuries-old trees absorb any light or matter. Moonlight, starlight, flashlights are no match for the darkness of the woods. Even sound ceases to travel farther than a few feet beyond the listener's ear. Here, there are only smells, the scent of things dying, decaying, and descending into hell. I throw my M-16 over my shoulder and start on my journey.

The walk down the dirt road to the chow hall isn't that far, I convince myself. It is only about half an hour, soldiers say it is only a mile. Without a rucksack, it should be an easy walk for someone used to rucking their body weight for hours. But in the dark, I am almost blind. Ruts, rocks, and roots trip me up. I switch on the red light of my flashlight hanging from the suspender of my LBE. From behind every tree, shadows lurk and threaten, but I have my M-16. It's not even loaded because this isn't a real deployment. We're just playing war games with our friends and allies. It's all make-believe, I tell myself. There's nothing to be scared of in these woods. No, not in the woods.

If I walk fast enough, it might be possible to catch up with Dale and Dix. I stretch my legs out beyond the crimson beam of my flashlight. The echoes of leaves and branches crunching under my boots march out of time behind me. I picture my two friends in no great hurry, meandering down the trail just ahead, cracking jokes and punching each other in the arm. Deep down, though, I know they are already out of the forest, seated at the chow hall.

Behind me, the sound of forest matter giving way under feet closes in. I step off the road. I grip at the strap of my rifle and turn my body to focus my flashlight out in the direction of the sound. The night gobbles up every speck of light. I can barely see beyond my boots. I walk on, keeping to the side of the patch, only to hear the footsteps again. Their pace quickens along with the beating of my heart. A man speaks out, but his words are unintelligible. As he comes closer another voice answers, but in Polish. Stepping off the road again, to the forest's edge, I flip off my light, but I can still make out their shapes.

The two men take up the width of the path. The loudness with which they speak conveys confidence. Well-fed, loud, confident, if the Polish Army is anything like ours, I figure they must be officers. They don't break their conversation to give any indication they know I'm holding my breath on the boundary of the woods. They pass without acknowledging my presence.

I let them walk on, putting distance between us before turning on my flashlight and stepping back onto the trail. My nose drips from the cold. I taste the salty mucus on my top lip. My armpits dampen and sweat trickles from between my shoulders down my spine. My polypro top feels like it is strangling me. I unzip the neck, but my chest burns from sucking in the cold air and panic. I put all the sensations out of my mind and keep marching.

There is a rustle in the treetops, an owl or some European fowl, perhaps. There is no hoot or caw. Everything goes quiet and I listen, but it is still. There's not the sounds of mice or other rodents running through the fallen leaves. The silence of the forest is as foreign to me as its black trees. The mountains of Eastern Kentucky that I loved exploring after dusk in autumn were alive. Trees rustled even in calm winds, fallen leaves moved underfoot, and animals called. The sounds comforted me and told me I was not alone in the world. Now I hear nothing but my own heartbeat.

I am in deep forest and deep shit. The woods are as disorienting as the labyrinth of boxes back in the motor pool bay. Based only on my internal sense of time and space I figure I have to be halfway to the dining facility. There's no turning back now. I should have been more rational and planned things out. Maybe I could have hidden from Sergeant Bluff on the Polish side of the motor pool. But I thought only of getting out of there, and finding Dale and Dix at the chow hall. I bolted straight into the woods like a scared rabbit. It's like I never heard stories about what happens to dumb little girls who go running off alone into dark forests.

Marching on, the rhythmic cadence of my　　　ssures me that each step gets me closer to my destinatio starts playing out of time as I hear a different me. I fall off to the side again and wait for th no one appears. I step back onto the road. rustle on the ground behind me as the fo step off the shoulder to let the person c with only silence.

"C'mon." The word comes out in a shaky whisper meant only for me. "Please. Go the fuck on."

My quiet plea is left unanswered. Stepping back onto the road, the footsteps begin again. Looking over my shoulder, I see nothing but darkness. I pick up my feet in an attempt to find the end or the beginning of this wormhole as fast as possible. The boots close in and speed up until we are marching together in perfect time. Terror rises up in me as I recognize the force of the toe strike, the way the heels hit the ground, the familiar sound of so much weight landing with a thud.

My M-16 bobs up and down on my shoulder, beating my back. I grip the strap to hold it down. I struggle to keep up this pace, to unsling my weapon. With the barrel in my right hand and stock in my left, I might catch my breath. My nearsighted eyes and the short wavelength red beam of my flashlight conspire against me. My toe snags on a root and I stumble forward, almost crashing face first into the ground. My thick winter boots, designed to keep frostbite away, threaten to drag me down to hell. Despite the danger, or because of it, I double-time, galloping in full battle-rattle in the pitch dark as fast as possible. The soldier is a heartbeat behind me. As he huffs and puffs his warm breath condenses on the back of my neck. His nonverbal utterances further give away his identity, and I know I have to lengthen my stride.

Another root or rock almost takes me out. What little eyesight I have is blotted out by lack of oxygen getting to my brain. My chest constricts and the muscles in my upper back spasm. My heart is pounding out of rhythm as it struggles to supply me with adrenaline and oxygen. Pain shoots through my injured left ankle and reminds me–I can't keep up this pace, even if my lungs were healthy. I stop. I can't go on. A month before my twenty-first birthday, this is how I die. I wonder if my stalker will kick my body the woods and tell everyone I went AWOL. Even in death I honored, labeled a coward, a deserter.

There is only one thing to do if I have any hope of getting out of here with my life and integrity. Fear is a hard knot in my throat. I swallow and it hangs in my chest before settling into the pit of my stomach. I turn around to face my threat. The massive hulk blocking out what little light gets through the trees, confirms what I already knew from his boots on the ground. The details of his face, the colors of his uniform are lost in the dark, but he is little more than meat and muscle, trunk and torso. I make out a head only when it eclipses some beam of starlight peeking through a branch.

As if by instinct, I call upon my training by some drill sergeant long ago. My muscles contract to do what they remember they need to do in such a situation. I plant my feet onto the ground, my right foot out in front, my left behind me. I draw my rifle back over my shoulder. I wrap my right hand over the barrel and grip the stock with my left. The butt of the weapon faces into the night, toward the shadow figure. My scream shatters the stillness. "Butt stroke to the groin. Butt stroke to the head," I say, repeating perhaps only in my mind, the mantra I learned during hand-to-hand combat training in Basic.

I tighten my grip on my M-16. The panic from my gut tries to rise and overtake me. My body shakes until I am certain I am in danger of falling to the ground in a fit. I can't let that happen, so I swallow as I look at death head-on. A man, or is it a wolf, moves toward me. I pull my raised weapon farther back over my shoulder. Its potential energy transfers into kinetic energy in to my hands and feet. I spring forward onto my toes.

Before I can strike, the man stumbles backwards as if falling over his own feet. He moves to his right, my left, staggering, tripping, nearly falling to avoid me. Keeping my eyes and weapon trained on him, I say nothing. I stand still ready to strike as he moves to the shoulder of the road. Without a word, only grunting and coughing, he walks past me in the direction of the chow hall. He disappears into the blackness as quickly as he came from it.

I march on in search of the light mounted on the pole just outside the chow hall that always tells us where we are, that we are almost there. I don't see it. I have no idea how much longer this march is going to take and every minute I stay in the woods the more dangerous it becomes. Mustering up everything I got I run and vow not to stop until I see that light.

When I come to a clearing, I see two tall lanky soldiers, laughing and joking as they make their way in my direction. I pray it is Dix and Dale, but their voices tell me otherwise. I stop before them gasping for breath, clutching my M-16. I am prepared if they are more foe than friend. But they stop talking and lean in toward me, as if about to ask me what happened.

My eyes fill up with hot tears. My body still twitches, but my legs feel like they might give way. I want to fall at their feet, crying and screaming, "Help me, please, oh God, help me. An animal, a beast, a man tried to attack me in the woods."

But I am a soldier, not a damsel in distress. There is no man with an axe to save me from a big bad wolf. I was trained to fight, to be strong. Unlike Mom said, no matter what, I will not break.

I regain my military bearing. I ask, "How much farther to the chow hall?"

The men look at each other, then me. One of the guys pointed toward the light, "Yeah. Right there is the light."

Against the clear dark sky shines a bright white light.

CHAPTER 22

YELLOW RIBBONS

The light is dying already, and it's barely past noon. Dale and Cox and I have little motivation left and the cold and dark setting in earlier and earlier does nothing for our morale. Dale whistles as he and Dix stand above me in an empty trailer, sweeping and tossing out whatever still remains of our mission to this God-forsaken place. I stack usable pallets onto the and pile broken pieces of trash onto the ground next to where the ice we dumped out after breakfast still sits unfrozen.

Recognizing the tune Dale sings as a cadence from basic, I join in with lyrics. My singing voice should probably get me court martialed, but I don't let that stop me from butchering the cadence, anyway. Loud and off-key, I croon:

> In her hair she wore a yellow ribbon,
> She wore it in the springtime, in the merry month
> of May,
> And if you ask her why the hell she wore it,
> She wore it for the soldier who was far, far away

. . .

"Incoming," Dale shouts as he sends a broken pallet crashing to the ground. "I hate that fucking cadence." He picks up a broom and sweeps like it was the trailer and not my voice that offended him.

"Hey, watch it," I say. "That's no reason to take me out with a pallet." I inspect it for damage before stacking it with the rest. "Beside you're whistling it."

"I wasn't whistling that one, I hate that one," he kicks a piece of wood with his boot, "Whoever wrote that one you're singing doesn't know how shit works in the real world. No one is sitting at home thinking about a soldier who's far, far away." He sings the last few lines in a high-pitched snarl and looks at Dix. "Do you have anyone worried about you?"

"Nah," Dix shrugs. Sitting down, his feet dangle off the back of the trailer. He picks up a part of the pallet. "My mom's too busy making sure my little retarded brother doesn't kill himself. He has to wear a football helmet, so he doesn't give himself a concussion. He'll bang his head against the wall or he'll beat himself over the head with whatever he can find." He picks up the piece of lumber and smashes it over his Kevlar until it breaks into splinters. "So, no. No one is thinking about me." His nervous laughter does little to fill in the horror of the silence as Dale and I stare, our mouths gaping. For what feels like an eternity we say nothing. We look away from one another.

"We got that one phone call when we first got here," Dale breaks the tension at last, "so I tried to call my girlfriend back in Bimbleberg. She said she was in the middle of watching German Big Brother with her parents, then she was getting ready to go out with her friends. I told her I was sorry for interrupting her night."

"Did you ever call her back, you know, since Sergeant Bluff let us have another call to let our families know we're coming home?" I ask.

"No." He shakes his head. "What's the use? It's too hard for civilians to understand what we go through. Especially Germans. I mean, look at your boyfriend and my girlfriend. They're our age, still living with their parents who still cook and clean for them like they're little babies. They don't have to worry about surviving, like we've had to. They know someone will always take care of them. Doesn't that bother you with your boyfriend?"

"Yeah. I mean sometimes."

"Most of us joined the Army as soon as we were old enough. We knew no one gave a shit. And they have the nerve to say shit like we're just out here camping or playing Army." Dale closes his eyes. He opens them again, but he still seems somewhere far away. "When I go back, I'm just going to break up with her. I think I need to be by myself for a while."

"Have you tried explaining it to her?" I ask.

Dale cocks his head to look at me. "C'mon, Burton." I stare at him. "Do you talk to your boyfriend? Have you called home since you've been here?"

"Yeah," I say. "I called home and talked to my mom when I first got here."

"That's good," Dale says with a bit of resentment in his voice.

"But, no, yeah, you're right," I admit. "It's like the Army brought us up here, then everyone sort of forgot about us. No one wants to even hear from us. It might disrupt their Saturday night." I snort, and my Kevlar bobs on my head. "When we first got here, I couldn't get ahold of my boyfriend. His mom said he was out with his friends. That's where he is, that's where he always is, hanging out with his friends in some warm bar, while I'm freezing my ass off in B.F.E. Poland."

Dale and Dix sigh, understanding.

"So I called my mom. She said I just caught her as she was walking out the door to a cookout. She said she had a few minutes, but she couldn't talk long. I was like, I don't have time to even wipe my ass on this mission, does she think I have time for dinner conversation?"

My buddies laugh.

"Anyway, so I said I guess the weather must still be nice in Kentucky if she can go to a cookout in October." I curl my frozen fingers up into my palms and tuck them under the opposite biceps. "She told me to have fun while I was in Poland. Have fun, can you believe that shit?"

"I didn't even call anyone." Dix stands up. "There's no one for me to call." He picks up a stave and holds it like a baseball bat. He swings it again and again, beating the side of the trailer.

"Jesus Fucking Christ, Dix," I holler. "Stop it. You're going to hurt somebody." The wood cracks and splinters. He hurls the large piece out across the distance. Dale howls with laughter and they high-five one another.

"You know how that cadence you were singing ends, don't you?" Dale stares down at me.

"No," I say. "I forget the rest of it."

"Something about some flowers, ain't it?" Dix asks.

"Oh, yeah. I think I remember now," I say. "Doesn't it go:

> And on his grave she laid some pretty flowers,
> She laid them in the springtime, in the merry
>   month of May,
> And if you asked her why the hell she laid them.
> She laid them for the soldier who was far, far
>   away"?

"All we get for what we've done is some flowers on our grave," Dale says.

"Don't forget that coin that Sergeant Major came by and handed out to us yesterday," I say, laughing.

"Yeah," Dale says. "Sergeant Bluff goes home with a fist full of awards while we get some token coin that don't mean shit from a Sergeant Major." He reaches into his pocket and pulls out the silver-dollar sized coin. He turns it around in his right hand a few times and tosses it up in the air. He pulls his shoulder back like he's throwing out the first pitch at a baseball game. He chucks the coin over my head where it is swallowed up by the Poland landscape.

"Dale." I look up at his bloodshot eyes, which are staring off into the distance after the coin. Dix chuckles. "How could you do that?"

"FTA, man." Dale picks up another large piece of wood. "Fuck the Army. I don't want to remember anything about this goddamn place." He brings down the wood, making it ring as he enunciates each syllable.

Dix laughs and repeats the mantra, "FTA, FTA." I wince and shield my face from the splintering wood. "Sayonara, motherfuckers. We're leaving."

"I've got a better cadence." Dale clears his throat and pats his chest. Standing on the edge of the trailer, he stretches out his arms and bellows:

> Sha na, na, na
> Na, na, na, na
> Hey, hey, hey,
> We're going home,
> Goodbye."

. . .

"I don't think it's going to be so easy to forget," I say, picking up some of the broken pieces. "I don't know how we will ever go home. I don't know if we *can* go back again."

CHAPTER 23

FOR SHAME

Back in Germany, after my mission to Poland, I try to unpack the shame I brought back with me. I can't explain it. I tell myself I didn't do anything wrong, but I know I must have done something to have caused everything that happened. If I hadn't been such a Shitbag to begin with, then Sergeant Bluff would never have taken me to Poland. If I hadn't laughed at Arkey's jokes, then he wouldn't have looked at me like that. The lurking around my cot at night, the refusal to let me have a latrine break, the keeping me away from my comrades to jump out at me from behind pallets, the chasing me through the woods... It was all so he could teach me a few lessons. He wanted to teach me about his power, his unchecked authority to do what he wanted with me and my body. He wanted to teach me what it means to be a woman in the Army. I imagine teaching him a few lessons with my M-16 or bayonet.

My comrades and I survived Poland only to be welcomed home not as comrades with honor, but as disgraces. There are no yellow ribbons, no parades, no families to welcome home soldiers like me. There is no unconditional love, no one who cares what we do so long as we come back safe, sound, and whole. Waiting for me here in Germany are the unshakable memories, the unforgivable thoughts. I open up my bags. I lay out all my gear. I strip myself naked. I throw both my body and gear into the harshest detergents and hottest water they can endure. I scrub until my knuckles are raw. No matter. The stain, the stench remains.

Every Thursday I report to formation carrying my humiliation like it is my TA-50, my field issue. My rifle is gone, turned into the arms room immediately upon my return. I tell myself I am free and light. But my armor is missing. I feel my M-16 like a phantom limb. I try to forget everything that happened, to lay down the guilt. But shame is another burden that I am doomed to ruck in the Army.

I did everything right. It wasn't my game, but I was forced to play it, learn its rules, and win. The only choice was to win. If I didn't win, I didn't come home. The rules were whatever he wanted them to be that day. That's okay, I told myself, because I am a soldier and I will adapt and overcome any obstacle. I will prove I am a real soldier.

Perhaps I was naïve to think there would be more time to be ready. I was naïve in think there would be more time to be ready. I proved I was ready because I wasn't ready to die.

I thought, perhaps he would be proud. I showed him I could win his game, the one he rigged for me to lose. When I cheated death, he cheated me out of my recognition. I get a slap in the face, a Certificate of Appreciation, nothing I can even wear on my uniform. Unlike my comrades in the other platoons, he gives me nothing. We made the mission a success with few people, little direction, and leadership who set us up to fail.

"You barely did your job," he said. "You don't deserve to be thanked for doing the minimum required of you."

I swallowed that hurt, the pain, the shame of always having to answer why I would never have a ribbon for my service in Poland when everyone else did. I would have to accept that he branded me so that I would always have to answer for what he did wrong. There was no choice.

When I came back I didn't expect a Hero's Welcome. A hot meal would have been nice. A long nap. A text from my boyfriend that said something besides, "I already made plans with my friends." A warm embrace. A soft bed.

Instead it was a cold, nasty rain as we worked to offload the vehicles from the railhead. It was my comrades Lemske and Peterson, who stayed behind with all their comforts, telling me Sergeant Bluff had driven a Humvee back instead of taking the long, slow train with the rest of us poor, stupid, dirty bastards. He beat us by hours and had time to plant his truth and let it grow before Dale, Dix, and I weeded out the lies.

"Poland was like a month-long party, we heard," Lemske breathed into my ear as I wrenched to free a Deuce and a half.

"How are the Polish men, Burton?" Peterson asked. "Are they as good as the Germans?"

With a wave of my wrench I sent the two women scuttling off like pests. They let words like "whore" and "slut" and "Shitbag" linger on the air after them.

My comrades and I knew the truth about Poland. The truth was not to be found in idle gossip. The truth did not reside in awards, accommodations, or medals. The truth was with us. We would stamp out the lies, the gossip where it started before it had time to burn through the company. We would ensure the truth became reality.

Outside the warehouse, as my buddies, Dix and Dale, and I offloaded more equipment from trucks I felt my own burden lifted. I knew the truth. I was a soldier, a real soldier, tested and proven. When Dix climbed atop the towering OD-green monster forklift to move an ISU storage unit, I conjured up my gung-ho and jumped behind to serve as ground guide.

"Yeah," Sergeant Bluff says now, as he leans into his second-in-command. His voice rises over the thumping of the forklift engine and drifts over to my ears as I motion for the forklift operator to back up. "Burton got her a little Polish sausage while we were up in Poland."

"Burton had some Polish sausage, huh?" Sergeant Samuels chuckles. I drop my hands and my focus. My head snaps toward my two platoon sergeants. They look back at me.

"Oops. I wasn't supposed to say that." A slow smile creeps across Sergeant Bluff's face as he glowers at me. "Oops. I let that slip."

The truth, what really happened, slips through my hands that I drop to my side. My motivation to continue in this capacity evaporates into the Bavarian winter air. I step aside and let Dale take my place. My will to fight this war is gone.

All day long I have felt the faint vibrations in my front BDU trousers pocket from texts that never come. I pull out my phone when Sergeant Bluff isn't looking to text my boyfriend, to call Mom back home. I will tell them both I don't need them. Then I decide the best way to show someone I don't care is to not call at all. I return to the warehouse, wearing my shame, the judging eyes of my world on me as I enter. My head held high past shaking heads, wagging tongues, my inner voice telling me I know myself, I know the truth, but knowing it was all for nothing.

My desire for strong drink and even a fight replaces my longing for a warm embrace, a hot meal, a kind word. What I want now is to put my fist into someone's face, throw myself on top of a man until ecstasy and pain blend, and top it all off with a strong drink. I want to destroy this world of mine. I want to destroy myself.

Tonight my buddies and I head out for a drink, looking to

reclaim something we lost when we went away. At Hermano's, my buddies disappear into the crowd, probably going home with some German girls they just met. It happens. Before the place closes, I make out with a boy barely a man, who asks first in German, then in English if I'll go with him. With my hair limp with sweat and mascara smeared under my eyes, I do my best to smile. In English, I tell him, "You don't want me." I kiss him and slip out the door where the frigid night air cuts through my thin clothes. Snow is in the air, and I can't remember if I left my coat inside or if I even wore it.

Down some back streets I stumble upon a footbridge over the River Reigen. Half-timbered buildings on the opposite banks jut out into the inky water. I have a blurry recognition of where I am, yet everything looks so different since I came home. A couple snuggled in chic black coats pass and stare with a mix of pity and resentment at my messy mop of red hair and sweaty makeup oozing off my face.

Somewhere, sometime I lost more than my friends and my coat.

With my fingers, I tear at my temples and cheekbones. I open my mouth. Like the alien-like figure in that famous painting I did a bad copy of in high school art class, I stand frozen on the bridge in a silent scream. As a teenager, I thought I understood the figure's loneliness. Now, as a soldier, I feel in my guts the swallowed pain that alienates, the hurt that makes a person start shrieking on a bridge.

Grabbing a hold of the railing, I step one foot up, then the other. The rail pushes its cold metal into my thighs as I lean forward. I wonder what it would be like to let go, to toss my shame, myself into the River Reigen. Below, foamy water breaks on unseen rocks in the black river.

CHAPTER 24

DADDY ISSUES

Some other soldiers in my platoon say I have issues. I will admit to some of that. But they have their own they will never acknowledge.

They say I am lazy, malingering, faking, lying. They say I am crazy, psycho, warped, even a buddy-fucker.

I don't admit to any of that, especially being a buddy-fucker. A buddy-fucker is a soldier who gets what they want even at the cost of his/her buddies. We have a few of those in this platoon. Peterson has never hesitated to throw her fellow soldiers under the bus.

As we all stand around the front of the warehouse, waiting to be released to go to stand outside in the cold November afternoon, her issues are on full display.

"Daddy," Specialist Peterson sings, leaning back into the dark pleather sofa intended for our military customers picking up supplies. The rest of the platoon stands around the front of the warehouse, waiting for Sergeant Bluff to dismiss us for final formation at seventeen hundred. "Me and Lemske are out here waiting for you. Daddy, are you coming?" Lemske shakes her blonde head and turns back toward the office. "Where you going, Lemske?" Peterson asks. "Tell Daddy to come out here."

Lemske's face flushes through dark caked-on makeup and heavy blush. "I'm not doing that. He's not my daddy."

"Uh-huh. Sergeant Samuels is your daddy. But Sergeant Bluff's your daddy, too."

Lemske gives a nervous laugh and her eyes move across the faces of everyone in the room. She looks at her friend sinking back into the couch. "You're acting crazy. What is wrong with you?"

Peterson perches herself on the arm of the sofa. Falling back onto the ripped cushions with wounds held together by drab olive reinforced packing tape, she kicks the heels of her combat boots over her head. "Daddy. Get out here."

Sergeant Bluff emerges from the office and walks to the side of the couch. He stops to look down at her. Her hair, with its ends splitting from being over-processed and over-styled with heating tools, splays across the cushions. She puts the soles of her boots down on the couch, arches her back, and purses her lips as if posing for the centerfold spread of Hot G.I. Babes Monthly. She smiles over at Sergeant Bluff before again kicking her feet up and grabbing hold of her combat boots. She points her ass up in the air and spreads her legs wide, revealing to all the stitched, reinforced crotch of her BDU trousers. She bats her eyelashes at our Platoon Sergeant and giggles, "Hi, Daddy."

I wait for him to give her an ass-chewing for such wildly inappropriate behavior while in uniform, on-duty. Instead, Sergeant Bluff's cheeks turn a soft, pale baby pink as he stares down at Peterson. Without a word he pulls his BDU cap from his trouser pocket and makes his way to the doors.

My mouth gapes open. I look at my buddies, Dale and Dix, to figure out what just happened. Dale's complexion turns a jaundiced yellow. Even Dix's smile fades as he watches the scene unfold.

It is as if someone dumped all the pieces of a jigsaw puzzle out onto the floor and they all magically fell into place. I think about it —the time Sergeant Bluff and Sergeant Samuels told me to be team player like all the other females; the Shitbag status I began occupying after that first meeting in the office; the reason why some soldiers never have to go to the field or do hard work in the back; the times in Poland that Sergeant Bluff put me in danger; now this daddy bullshit Peterson is pulling. I can't believe it has taken me over ten months in this place to see how everything finally makes sense, but at last it does.

For too long, I wanted to believe the Army, our Army, the United States Army, was above certain things. Our male soldiers, especially those in charge, were far too honorable to treat the women in their ranks, their fellow soldiers, as little more than animals to be used as they saw fit for their pleasure or abuse. Someone like me, I thought, would be too disgusting to worry about being attacked should such a thing happen in the Army.

But it isn't like the movies at all. It isn't about a man seeing a woman so enticing that she becomes his obsession. Because of her beauty he is so overcome by desire that he cannot help himself. He becomes an animal. The truth is that a woman becomes a target for no other reason than because she refuses the man, she says no. The man is determined to make her submit, completely, fully, or else destroy every piece of her.

I hate Peterson for giving Sergeant Bluff what he wants, for fucking all of us over, especially me, her fellow woman. Because she did what a man in charge wanted, because it gave her an easier life in the Army, she surrendered to him. She, as well as Lemske, have joined in with him to the point that my life has been put in danger. They could have been stronger. They could have said no. We could have been stronger if we had stuck together, but they only thought of themselves.

I am broken. The Army has broken me, like Mom said. I am

not strong. I wish I had just given in, given up, given that man what he wanted. I could have avoided all this. Maybe it is too late. I wonder if I say I changed my mind, if the fear, the threats, the Shitbag status might vanish in an instant. My life in the Army would change. I could coast through to better assignments, even promotions. Life would be tolerable, even pleasant.

But that is a fairy tale. I couldn't give my father what he wanted and I can't give Sergeant Bluff what he wants. Besides, it is too late now. The damage is done to both my body and mind. None of this can be undone. I fear I won't even live through my first—and I must face it—only enlistment. Any dreams I had of making a career in the Army are dead. My only thought is of saving myself and my buddies. I can't do what Peterson and Lemske did. It would only make everyone's lives harder.

I stare at Peterson on the couch, still cackling. It's a car wreck I can't look away from. She is broken. She is broken in so many places. Sergeant Bluff is broken. The whole Army is broken. There isn't enough duct tape to put any of them back together.

I am not broken and I refuse to shatter.

CHAPTER 25

GRENADES IN GLASS HOUSES

As if a grenade just went off inside his office, Sergeant Bluff's voice rattles my nerves and the glass windows behind his head. Unlike when I was in here right after my arrival back in January, he leaves the door open this time. On this chilly December morning he wants an audience. This is a public trial.

My mind wanders like a radio dial, tuning past static and noise until it lands on some pleasant, unoffending Christmas tune. *Jingle horse, jingle horse, pick up your feet.* my foot taps out the silent beat.

The tune in my head drowns out his message, but I can guess. He is accusing me of *never* being at work. He claims I am *always* hiding in the latrine, or *always* going to sick-call, or *always* going to an appointment and *always* leaving my comrades to pick up the slack. I am ordered to Parade Rest and to listen in silence while he makes these charges. I am not permitted to present evidence or witnesses on my behalf. I am already guilty and he has decided this is how he will punish me. My comrades listening outside will decide later.

My eyes land on the table-top Christmas tree perched on top

of the filing cabinets. Collecting black dust on its ornaments and its tiny twinkling lights burning under the harsh fluorescent office bulbs, it seems too innocent to bear witness to all this, yet it serves its purpose.

"Specialist Burton," Sergeant Bluff asks, "what are you smiling about?"

"No reason, Sergeant."

He dismisses me. Outside the office I make my way past all the brand new soldiers in the Issue Section gawking up at me.

I try to ignore the stares and instead think about diving into my work for the day, the month, the rest of this year. I can't wait to rip the last page from the desk calendar and toss it in the trash. One year down, one to go in this shithole.

"Psst, Burton," a soft voice whispers as I walk through the Issue Section. A foot juts out into my path, nearly tripping me.

"What the fuck? You trying to kill me or something?"

I trace the foot up to a young soldier who has rolled her chair back from her desk. The name tag on her BDU top says Romero and the rank on her collar are the skeeter wings of a Private First Class. She's one of a handful of new Privates I barely know here in the SSA. Sergeant Bluff must have put in a bulk order for young, new soldiers fresh from training and they started showing up while we were gone to Poland.

"Sorry." She glances around, then looks up at me with Bambi eyes. "What did Sergeant Bluff talk to you about?"

"What's it to you?" I stare back until she looks away. "Are we friends or something?"

Her boots look like she took a Hershey Bar to them and her wrinkled BDUs pull tight across her body. Her eyes still sparkle and her face still has a soft pink glow. Even with her hair pulled tight in a bun, it isn't hard to see it must drape in luxurious waves around her shoulders when she lets it down.

"I want to talk to you about something." She smiles,

revealing baby fat cheeks. I frown, feeling the tug of gravity at the loose skin of my jowls. I'm aging in here and it shows. Perhaps I am envious of her, her beauty. Peterson always said Sergeant Bluff puts the ugly soldiers in the back to hide them. Maybe because Romero is beautiful, Sergeant Bluff chose her to work in the front. But I also wonder if it's because she's a "team player" like Peterson and Lemske that she is up here. I hate her for what I only wonder is true.

"I don't have time to talk." I check my watch. "Ask someone else. I'm just some dumb, ugly Shitbag who works in the back. I don't know nothing."

"Wait." She grabs my arm.

I pull back my arm and snarl like a feral dog, "What? What do you want?"

"This shit ain't right." She glances up and around the room as if to see if anyone is listening. "The stuff that goes on in here. What *he* does... Some of us have been talking about it."

"Hmmm, really?" I shift my weight from my bad left foot to my right. My hatred boils. I have convicted her in my mind and judged her sentence appropriate. Like Peterson or Lemske, she could have refused the terms of our sergeant's agreement. She didn't want to be a Shitbag like me, but now she realizes, perhaps, the cost of working up here is too great.

"Yeah." She leans forward. "We decided we're going to call the IG." She leans back in her chair and smiles.

"That's a fucking waste of time," I say. "I've been here almost a year and the Inspector General's been called more times than I can count. Nothing ever happens."

"Why not?" Her face goes pale.

"Because here's what happens," I say. "Somebody files a complaint on Sergeant Bluff. The IG says they're coming to conduct interviews. Then Sergeant Bluff calls us into his office to tell us he will make our lives fucking hell if we talk. So everyone clams up by the time they're asked to give statements."

I pause, take a breath, then continue. "Last time he threatened to put us on around-the-clock rotating shifts in the SSA, make us pull duty on holidays and weekends, deny all leave, force us to eat MREs instead of going to chow, conduct random white-glove inspections in the barracks, and let's see what else..."

Staring up at the ceiling, I try to recall the laundry list of items he threatened us with. "Oh, yeah, he said, 'I will run your asses to the castle and back every morning.' That's an exact quote."

I let out a belly laugh. Then I stare straight into Romero's amber eyes. "Do you know what that's like? I do. It's the equivalent of running a 10K across broken, uneven pavement, straight up then down a mountain."

"He can't do that stuff." She stares back at her computer monitor and moves the mouse around on the desk. "That's against the law."

"What law? There's no law. He can do whatever he wants to us. Maybe if you had been in Poland with us, you'd understand."

"Well..." She bats her eyelashes and stares at the concrete floor. "I've already told my mom everything. She said there has to be a law against what's going on in here. She's going to call our congressman."

"That's nice." Bending my knees, I lift one foot at a time off the floor. I stretch my arms. "I'm glad you talked to *your* mom— mine doesn't want to hear about it anymore. But the truth is unless your mom's married to the congressman, he doesn't give a shit." Her face pales. "*No one* gives a shit about us in here. We are disposable. Sergeant Bluff even said it himself, how there would be no investigation if he had to lose a few of us along the way since we signed up to die. That's what we're here for, he said." Her complexion turns a sour yellow, almost green.

She looks up at me, and her face falls. "I can't take it anymore.

I can't take what he's doing to us."

"What do you have to be so worried about?" I roll my eyes. "He's tapped you to be one of the soldiers who works up front. You have a good life. You're already deemed 'too essential' to ever go to the field for 'extra training'. He'll never sentence you to hard labor in the back of the warehouse because you're an ugly Shitbag like me."

She scrunches up her nose, like she might cry, then pulls her arms and legs close to herself. "I'll get pregnant and get out." She steadies her trembling lip. "I'm single, so if there's no one to take care of the baby the Army has to let me out."

"Really?" I ask. "You want to get pregnant? How old are you?"

"Eighteen."

"Eighteen? Jesus Fucking Christ."

"So? Lots of women my age have babies."

"Yeah, back in the olden days, up the hollers where I'm from." I shake my head. "But it's the new millennium. No one does that now. Don't be fucking stupid."

"I'm not stupid," she grins. "If we can join the Army at eighteen, then we can have a baby."

"I joined the Army at seventeen," I say. "I just turned twenty-one last month. After all the bullshit I've been through in here, I feel like I'm about seventy-one. But I know I'm still too young for a kid. A baby will ruin your damn life."

"The Army will ruin my life," she mutters, pooching out her lip. "A baby that I'd love forever would never ruin my life."

"The Army is for four years, a kid is for life," I say. "How are you going to afford to raise a child when the Army kicks you out?"

"I don't know." She raises her chin and shoots me a defiant look. "I'll find a way. My mom will help me. It'll work out."

"Yeah?" I ask. "When you come home after work and there's no money, the house is filthy, the baby is crying, and the dad is, where?" I pause for a moment. "When it's not a baby anymore, when it's a kid, you'll say how easy things would have been, if only..." I scratch at my scalp, feeling the dirt the shampoo didn't get out. "I know how that makes a kid feel. I'd never do that to a child."

"I would never do that either." Her eyes watering, she hisses the words at me.

"But you want to have a baby just so you can get out?"

"I want a baby someday, so why not now?" She shrugs.

"Everyone in here says females can just get pregnant and get out if they don't like it." I sigh hard. "Even my own family used to say women got pregnant in the Gulf War just to get out because they were too chicken-shit to handle combat."

Her eyes widen, then narrow. "My oldest sister was in the Gulf War. She wasn't too scared to fight. She's why I joined."

"Yeah?" I ask. "I used to watch the news and see all those female soldiers driving trucks across the desert. I wanted to be like them. They were so tough, so brave. They didn't have to just be wives or mothers."

"I wanted to be a soldier, but I also wanted to be a mom. Someday." She swallows hard. "But I'm not sure I can be a soldier anymore. Maybe if we just go talk to someone and tell them..."

"Tell them what?" I ask. "No one is going to save us. Not our moms or a baby, and especially not a congressman, or some officer. No one is going to throw themselves on a grenade to save us. It's on us. I already learned a long time ago that if I want to live to get out, I have to take care of myself."

"I didn't come in here just to get out..." She hesitates. "But maybe getting out is the only option now."

Softening my tone, I say, "A woman in the Army is damned no matter what choice she makes." At that moment, I realize the truth in that statement. When Romero stares back at me, I wonder how long ago she realized that truth.

CHAPTER 26

FORGIVE AND FORGET

They say there are no atheists in the foxhole, but what faith I had in God evaporated while I was in Poland. There, I contemplated the nature of God. At first I imagined He must be on the side of the Army, working alongside Sergeant Bluff, to punish Dale, Dix, and me for being Shitbag soldiers. Then, halfway through, while we starved among the stacks of food, while our skin ached from layers of filth, my prayers for forgiveness went unanswered. I determined He, like everyone else, must have forgotten us. At last, near the end of the mission, I realized there is no God. There is only Man and his infinite cruelty.

But, hallelujah. My faith is restored. I've been saved. It feels like some miracle. It is Christmastime and I want to shout, "I believe, I believe." Sitting behind an old heavy metal desk, in my freshly starched BDUs and highly shined boots, I'm basked in the clean, white, electric glow of the fluorescent lights overhead. New year, new Burton. I fire up the tower computer that sits by my feet and the boxy monitor on the desk. The screen flickers and displays the words ULLS-G in its 8-Bit Nintendo-like glory.

Plucked from obscurity, from certain death in Sergeant Bluff's SSA, I've been reassigned to the motor pool. No longer am I some nobody slinging pallets in the back of the warehouse. Now I am in one of the most-coveted positions in my field. I'm a maintenance and supply clerk, managing inventory and vehicle repairs, answering phones, typing memos, giving status reports to Captain Gross, our company commander, and bigwig Master Sergeants up at Battalion. This job requires a smart soldier, a good-looking soldier, a squared away soldier. Only that kind of soldier, not a Shitbag like me, would have a chance in hell of getting this job and escaping Sergeant Bluff.

This assignment is what I've been working for, although I thought my hard work might never pay off. It's what I've been praying for, although I long ago gave up on praying. It is a miracle from God, divine intervention.

Late last summer, during that ass-smoking I got in the warehouse for being late, my belief in God was hanging on by a thread. In my moments on the floor, spitting warehouse dirt out of my mouth while my comrades, even my buddies looked on and laughed, I prayed. I asked God not to make it stop, but to help me understand what I did to deserve the humiliation, the punishment. I prayed that I would understand how I had angered him, what I had done wrong so that I might make amends, so that I could square things away. Receiving no answer and seeing no end to my pain, I asked to speak to the Chaplain.

Sitting in scratchy flannel chairs across from the holy officer, Captain Clement, in his office I confessed to everything, even the most terrible thing a soldier can be. "I'm just a Shitbag soldier, Sir."

I focused on the tips of his collars, unable to look at him while I spoke those words. On his right-hand side there were his Captain Bars. On his left-hand side, he wore a subdued iron-on cross. Whether or not it was supposed to, those mismatched insignia always symbolized to me that a Chaplain was both an Army officer as well as a clergyman. On that day, I hoped Captain Clement was more clergyman than Captain.

"I made a mistake signing my name on that dotted line and joining the Army. I can't take it anymore," I said.

My face flushed under the streaks of warehouse dust. I stared down at my smudgy boots and tried to hide them by digging my toes into the carpet. My hands were in worse shape, so I picked at my dirty fingernails. Catching a whiff of my sweaty underarms, I held my arms close to my sides. I sat quiet after my statement, wishing my meeting with the Chaplain had been in the morning before I'd reported to work. Instead there I sat in filth and humiliation, proving that I was a dirty, Shitbag soldier.

Captain Clement nodded. I stared into his face. He seemed so much older than our company commander, Captain Gross, who reminded me of that kid in class who wouldn't sit at his desk. Yet somehow, with his rounded jawline and smooth features, the Chaplain looked younger than our commander.

"You do seem tense whenever I've seen you around." Behind his thick lenses encased in plastic grandpa aviator frames, his eyes took on a puppy-dog appearance.

"I am stressed, ir." I stared at the wall across the room.

Absent from this room were the cross-stitched Bible verses I often saw hanging in the country churches in which I grew up. There weren't any pictures or plaques related to the Army displayed on his desk or tacked to the wall. Standing against the wall was a fake green plant that looked like nothing I'd ever seen in nature. It was warm, too warm for August in Germany. There was no window, or if there was, it was camouflaged with curtains or mini-blinds, causing it to blend in with the wall. Hanging on the wall near the desk was a diploma I eyed with envy. If only I'd stayed in college and gone to ROTC, then I'd be sitting in a nice, clean office.

"They make fun of me for *being stressed*, Sir," I continued. "They ask me all the time, 'Are you stressed, Burton? You ain't got nothing to be stressed about. It ain't like you ever been down range.'"

"Well," he said. "I've counseled a lot of soldiers who have been to Kosovo."

"Yes, Sir?" I asked.

He shrugged. "Deployments can be stressful for a lot of soldiers, just like being in garrison can be stressful."

I took a breath and looked at him, trying to decide if I should reveal the next thing. Hearing my NCOs' voices in my head, in my best snarling, mocking tone, I said, "They're always saying, 'You want to request to speak to the Chaplain, Burton? Go tell him how you're feeling?'"

Shutting his eyes, he leaned back in his chair. He chuckled and his belly jiggled like a more reserved version of Santa Claus.

"Sorry, Sir."

"It's okay." His cheeks turned into little round apples.

"I'm just so sick of it." I paused. "I know I'm not perfect, but they are torturing me. They are just fucking with me to see if they can break me." My eyes widened, and I looked up at the Chaplain. "I'm so sorry, Sir. I didn't mean to cuss. It's such a habit." I looked back down at the floor and shook my head. Not only did I look and smell like a Shitbag, but I must sound like one, too.

"I'm in the Army," he said. "I've heard much worse."

"I have messed up a few times, Sir, I admit it. I was late for duty, I don't show leadership abilities, I don't get my boots shiny enough, but I don't think it's right how they're punishing me." My voice trembles. I follow his gaze to the box of Kleenex on the scuffed particle board table between us. My eyes widen in recognition at the Star of David-like pattern embossed on the tabletop. Mom had two of these in our living room growing up.

"Sir." I steady my voice. I am a soldier, on my own in a foreign country. I don't need Kleenexes. "I'm one of the hardest workers in the SSA. I bust my ass in the back of that warehouse, but they say I'm lazy and I'm riding sick-call so I don't have to work. I have a high score on my ASVAB and they laugh at me and call me stupid. I'm also one of the highest-ranking Specialists in the platoon, but they make me stand at the end of the formation after everyone, even a Private. They tell me I'm just a Shitbag. And they tell everyone else if you don't want to end up like Burton, then you'd better not do what she does."

My nostrils flared and my lower lip trembled. If I'd been alone in a soundproof room, I would have screamed until I lost my voice. I would have picked up a chair and thrown it against the door. I would have made King Kong seem a little flustered. Instead, I fixed my gaze straight ahead and tried to maintain some dignity. "Sir, I can't take it anymore. I don't know why God is punishing me."

Captain Clement took a deep breath and let it out. "I don't think God is punishing you."

"I knew you'd say that, Sir." Snorting, I shook my head. "No offense."

The edges of his mouth turned downward, and he cocked his head to one side.

Waves of nausea pounded my stomach lining. If he only knew about the night I hung over the bridge contemplating throwing myself into an icy, rushing river, he would know that not only was I a Shitbag soldier, but that God indeed hated me and was punishing me.

He leaned forward, putting his forearms on his large thighs. "How can we figure out a way to help you?" he asked.

My eyes darted around the room as I thought of an answer. "Please don't ask me to pray," I said, the only words that came to my brain, "because I've tried that and it isn't working, Sir."

"I never ask anyone to pray unless they want to." His features softened.

"I don't know, Sir." I shifted my butt to sit up straight. "I don't know what anyone can do to help. I just want to get away from Sergeant Bluff. I want to get out."

That's when I remembered. A new position was being created in our company. A ninety-two alpha logistical specialist was needed to assist my former squad leader, Sergeant Westen, down in the motor pool. Some said it would only go to a Sergeant, others said it was going to be open to Specialists. Some even said the job had been created especially for Peterson. They said her ASVAB scores were shit, and she did nothing all day, but she had worked her way into it by "cleaning" Sergeant Bluff's office. However, others said she was so at ease speaking with the First Sergeant, her PT scores so good, and her uniform always squared away, she was the right choice to hobnob with Captains and Master Sergeants. Whatever the truth, the one thing we all could agree on was that Shitbags in the back need not apply.

I mentioned the new slot to the Chaplain, but I said, "They'd never even consider me, Sir. I mean the First Sergeant doesn't even know I exist. If he does, I'm sure Sergeant Bluff has told him some things about me."

"Maybe you should give First Sergeant Dean some credit," he said. "I know him and he seems fair."

I shrugged.

"However, if you think he doesn't know you that well, maybe you should let him know who you are."

"No, Sir." I broke out in a cold sweat at the suggestion. "There's no way I can talk to the First Sergeant. I don't know what I'd even say."

"Okay, then." He looked up at the ceiling or heaven, then back at me. "Do you think you could write something?"

I smiled. I had written my way out of a shit ton of trouble with the MPs after that forklift incident. Hell, yeah, I could write something.

He recommended that I send a letter to First Sergeant Dean telling him who I was and why I deserved to get that job. Then he'd talk to him on my behalf and see about getting me transferred away from Sergeant Bluff. I thanked the Chaplain as I got up to leave, but I knew our plan was doomed to fail. There was no way I could craft a piece of pure fiction masquerading as nonfiction, outlining what a high-speed soldier I was. Still, I had to try.

Not long after our meeting, I headed over to the base's MOS library. The ancient librarian who looked like he'd haunted the place since the end of World War II didn't ask many questions. I told him I needed information about the Ninety-Two Alpha military occupational specialty. I struggled at the computer sweating, typing, deleting, and retyping a letter spelling out all the great things I'd done in the Army. But nothing. There was nothing to write because I hadn't done anything. I hadn't deployed; I hadn't earned any medals. I was not exceptional in any way.

It was true, I was just a fucking Shitbag. I was going to die in that fucking platoon if I didn't find a way to get out. I wanted to put my head in my hands and cry, but even at the library someone is always watching. I had to keep it together. I stared at the cursor mocking me. At last, I started listing from the MOS book the things I did every day as a Ninety-Two Alpha. That's when it occurred to me I was writing a resume. I asked the librarian for a book on resumes and he gave me a couple softcovers.

I threw everything in that document. Not only did I include my current MOS as a Ninety-Two Alpha and its duties, but I wrote about my Eighty-Eight Mike truck driving MOS from the Reserves, I listed my high school classes, my year at college, even my civilian jobs. Then, I included my only awards, the one every soldier gets for completing AIT, the Service Ribbon, and a Certificate of Achievement for working the supply point in Former East Germany. Finally, I wrote a letter to the First Sergeant explaining how my skills and abilities learned through my education and civilian and military work experience would make me a valuable asset to the motor pool. I prayed he'd see the me I put on the page and not the one presented by Sergeant Bluff.

Days, weeks, then months passed without a word. I heard the job had been nixed. I heard our commander had vetoed every soldier First Sergeant Dean recommended. I heard someone say we are all going to die so nothing mattered, anyway.

I was afraid I might die sooner than some others. I needed out. I needed away from all my superiors, my comrades, even my buddies who'd turned on me. I prayed for God to ease my pain, to help me escape before Sergeant Bluff packed me along with Dale and Dix off to Victory Strike Poland 2000 with him. Life seemed unbearable. I felt like I didn't have a friend in the world. Even after my buddies apologized, it took us going off to Poland to help heal the rift. Even with them by my side, I didn't think I would make it home. I prayed for God to help us, to send someone to stop Sergeant Bluff, but He didn't listen. God forgot about us and left us to die. Everyone forgot us—the Chaplain, the First Sergeant, everyone. So I forgot about this motor pool job and focused on surviving the warehouse.

Then one day, as the sun set while we all stood shivering in final formation late one Friday afternoon last month Sergeant Bluff announced, "Burton will report to the motor pool formation from now on." After formation, when I attempted to ask for clarification, he said, "If you have any questions you can direct them to Sergeant Ruiz. He's in charge of the motor pool."

"I guess I'm moving to the motor pool." I stood dazed, soldiers rushing past to get on with their weekend. I couldn't believe it. My talk with the Chaplain had paid off. He must have gone to bat for me and his advice about writing to the First Sergeant must have worked. I wondered if there really was a Santa Claus, or even a God, after all.

"Congratulations." Dale slapped me on the arm. "You're getting out of the SSA. You're going to be with Sergeant Westen, another one who got out, but said he'd always have our backs. But we barely talk to him now. Guess you got pretty lucky, huh?"

"Yeah," I grinned, still shocked. "I mean—"

"Hey, man." Dale grabbed Dix by the shoulders and gave him a jiggle as he walked up. "Let's skip the chow hall and eat in town. Then we go straight to the club after that. It's payday. Dolla, dolla bill."

Dix nodded and grinned a baby-toothed smile. "Cash money."

I cocked my head to one side. "What was that?"

"You ain't never heard that song before?" Dale asked. "Damn, where you been?"

"No," I chuckled. "Probably not born yet when your old ass was listening to it."

Dale shook his head. "Dix knows it and he's younger than you." Dix rolled his eyes at me. "That's because we know good music. We're not listening to that techno shit anymore they play over here in Germany. That shit's for pussies."

"Okay. I thought we all loved techno…"

I watched my two buddies walk off together without answering. And without me. I watched until they were out of sight and then I turned in the opposite direction, making my way to the other end of the basketball court where Sergeant Westen and Sergeant Ruiz and the last few mechanics of the motor pool platoon were still gathered. They were my people now. I couldn't think about what, or who, I was leaving behind.

Now as I sit behind my new old desk here in the motor pool office the light bounces off the spit-shined toe of my boot. I run my finger down the stiff crease lining the shin of my trousers and I can almost smell the starch from the cleaners. My auburn pixie cut has grown out into a shag, smells not of industrial grit, but instead of a crisp spring rain or a lush tropical waterfall or some such thing my shampoo promises, when I run my hands through it.

At last, I've finally got what I've always wanted. I have escaped. I have survived. I wonder if I have at last been washed clean, if I'm finally forgiven for whatever sin or sins I've committed. I don't know if I should thank Man or God or the Army for all this. Maybe I have only myself to thank for everything that's happened in here. Somehow, I don't think Man, God, or the Army is ready to forgive or forget anything just yet.

CHAPTER 27

SICK AND TWISTED

My eyes flickered open, but in this dark space I saw nothing. I was tethered to something, a bed, a pole. I thrashed, kicking off the covers. I knew only that I needed to get out of there, but I was too weak to escape. The bed seemed to spin and flames threatened to engulf my entire body. Something cold dripped into my veins, chilling my whole body.

In both flanks of my mid-lower back was the sensation of someone stabbing me over and over again. I wondered why I didn't die. Someone, a woman, next to me in the dark room moaned as if pleading for help. I heard the sound of a door opening, feet shuffling. I patted my bed, looking for my M-16, but I couldn't find it. I lay still to not bring attention to myself. I was too weak to fight without a weapon. I had no idea where I was. This didn't look like Poland or even the field. Maybe I died. Maybe I was in hell.

Turns out I wasn't in hell, but instead a German hospital. When I finally got a hold of my senses, the doctor told me I had an infection in my kidneys that was close to traveling throughout the rest of my body. I said I still didn't understand. They told me I had a fever, and I just needed to rest.

"The Army is going to kill me," I said. "I can't stay here. They will say I have gone AWOL. They are going to make my life a living hell if I don't call and ask them if it's okay."

The old gray-haired doctor raised his voice. "No," he said. "You don't need to call and ask the Army if you can go to Hospital. The Army almost killed you, already. They almost let you die."

I didn't die, and I didn't go to hell. Perhaps I should be grateful to God or the German medical system or whoever for saving my life, but I don't know why I've been saved. I lived only to come back to the Army, a place that makes the Christian notion of hell feel like going on leave for R & R. It is peacetime. Germany. And I've only been on Active Duty a year and some change, but I am plagued by the sense that death will catch up to me soon.

I thought my job at the motor pool was my salvation, but just over a month since getting here, I realize I will never be safe from Sergeant Bluff's reach. Even though I am no longer in his platoon, because he outranks me I still answer to him. He calls me out whenever he sees me in formations, road marches, or PT. He is still in charge of certain things, like the barracks, and he puts me on duty whenever he can. He huddles with other NCOs, whispers, and laughs whenever I cross his line of sight. My name is always on his lips and he continues to humiliate me in front of not only my comrades, but my superiors. I worry his words have infected my new platoon, especially the L.T.

The copy of my hospital discharge paper I keep in my BDU pocket is already creased and dirty from my fingers. Every few minutes I pull it from my trouser pocket. I touch it to make sure it's still there. I reread it just to make sure it's real. Written by a German doctor, an authority on the matter, it says, "Burton is not a Shitbag." It is my only proof, my only protection, since the doctor on base, Captain Cooke, fought giving me a profile since he would have to wait for the records to be translated and that could take days or weeks. When I told him that the word pyelonephritis was the same in English as it is in German, he declared me cured of my kidney infection and cleared me for all duty since my discharge from the hospital.

The familiar scent of grease and oil hangs in the cold, still air of the motor pool when I return to work that morning. Sometimes the quiet in the Army causes my heart to beat so hard it hurts. My mind imagines angry higher-ups who will arrive to find that my mere presence disgusts them, and it will set them off. I imagine the insults they might, and often do, rattle off. Other days, alone in the motor pool I have time to organize my thoughts and files before the day starts. Sergeants Westen and Ruiz don't scream, but my nerves have yet to settle.

Perhaps it is best I didn't get a profile. After being in the hospital for a week, there are sharks circling, no doubt vying for this position. I rummage through a stack of papers on the desk and find a ten-page inventory report dated from late last week. If I can get a good start on it before Sergeant Westen and Sergeant Ruiz come in, I can remind them why they chose me.

In the motor pool bay, I work my way down the inventory list. It is an Army scavenger hunt with names like ASSY, GENERATOR, which could be anything and no assigned location. I check the toe tags of various greasy engine parts sitting on the floor. Despite my love of driving trucks, I have learned little about their guts.

A huge hunk of metal sits on a pallet on the floor. The toe tag that lists its part number and name has fallen off and underneath it. I give the part a tug and feel my back spasm. "Goddamn it." I grab my knees. "What is this fucking thing, anyway?"

"What are you doing to that alternator?" a stern, male voice asks.

I straighten myself up to see our platoon leader, Lieutenant Perry, standing over me, his cap bearing the gold bar of his rank. He reeks of the cigarette he was smoking outside the bay doors before he came in. As he stares down at me, two vertical lines form between his brows. He may only be in his late twenties, still old for a second lieutenant, but his chain-smoking isn't doing him any favors.

"Oh." I squint at the thing I've been fighting with on the floor. It doesn't look anything like the alternator I helped replace in my old Nissan back in Kentucky. "Good morning, Sir. I was just getting a head start inventorying these parts."

"Have you decided to rejoin us?" he asks. "Are you out of the hospital now?"

Brushing off the sarcasm, I laugh, "Yes, Sir." I pat myself down. "It sure looks like I'm back."

"Hmm." He stares somewhere around my abdomen. "And are you done pissing blood, too?" Without waiting for a response he walks off toward his office, leaving me to fight with the alternator.

When the platoon of mechanics files into the bay I am still conducting my inventory. I smile, happy to see the guys again, but one by one they freeze before me, going mute in my presence. Some guys stare wide-eyed at me; others try to stammer out a few words and blush before giving up to go get their tools and coveralls. I wonder if they are embarrassed they didn't come to see me in the hospital. I was glad Sergeant Westen, Sergeant Ruiz, First Sergeant Dean, and even my company commander, Captain Gross stopped by, but it would have been nice if one of my comrades had taken a few minutes to visit. I fold up the inventory sheets and turn away.

"Hey, Burton," someone says. "You weren't in PT this morning."

I turn to see PFC White standing there in his dirty, crumpled BDUs first thing in the morning after a holiday weekend. I wonder if he ever bothers to wear coveralls when he's crawling under the Five-Tons and Humvees.

"Oh, wow," he says. "I didn't know you were back."

"Yep," I say. "I was just in the hospital. I didn't die and rise from the grave."

"Oh, yeah, well." He fiddles with a wrench. "Sergeant Bluff said..."

"What the fuck did he say now?"

"He's in charge of the barracks, you know?" White giggles and looks away.

"Uh-huh."

"So, he told me that as soon as you got out of the hospital that we needed to come and find him about new room assignments."

"Wait." I shake my red shaggy bob that seems to have become wild and unmanageable in just one week away from the Army. "He wants us to swap? But you're on the first floor. That's an all-male floor."

"Not swap," he says. "While you were gone, he decided to rearrange the barracks."

"Rearrange them how?"

"He said he's been violating Army regulations this whole time."

"Ha," I say. "That's fucking rich."

"Males and females can't be segregated, he said. So he decided to group the floors by platoon. The motor pool is all together on the first floor."

"How do all those guys fit on one floor?"

"He has some of us doubled-up now in the big rooms. That's why he needs to see me and you. Because you are the only female, he has to give you my small room and I have to move into one of the bigger rooms with a roommate."

"So now there are empty rooms on the second and third floors because there aren't enough soldiers in those platoons to fill them up, but he has guys doubling up on the first floor?"

White shrugs.

"And where am I supposed to even shower or shit or take a piss? There's no female latrine on the first floor. I just got out of the hospital yesterday. The doctors have me drinking two liters of water a day. I'm going to have to march my ass up a flight of stairs in the middle of the night?"

He shrinks inside his oversized BDU top. I look over his head at the rest of the mechs in the bay. Gone are the jokes and the "Hey, Burton"s I have grown used to as they walk about getting tools or supplies.

I stare at White. "Why is everyone acting so weird? What is going on in this fucking place?" He shrugs. "Our asshole L.T. didn't even come see me in the hospital, yet he had the nerve to come up to me this morning and... Like I don't even know how he knew... What have people been saying while I was gone?"

"I don't know. I try not to listen to stuff." White looks up at me. "But Sergeant Bluff said some stuff."

I swallow hard. "What did he say?"

"He said, well, he said, you were in the hospital for an STD."

"What the fuck? Are you kidding me?"

"He said you got an STD because you were fucking all those Polish soldiers on Victory Strike, then you came back to Germany and you fucked a bunch of German guys."

"That's bullshit." I feel the hot sting of tears about to betray me. "I didn't fuck anyone in Poland. And I have one boyfriend who is German. Not that it's anyone's business who I fuck."

White is silent.

"So everyone thinks I'm a whore, and that's why they won't talk to me now?"

"Well, he said some other stuff, too."

I close my eyes and shake my head. "What other stuff did he say? I want to know, so spit it out."

"He said it would say something about us if we were seen with you."

"What?"

"Yeah, he said females had always been bad for the military, going all the way back to, like, World War I or II and then in Vietnam. Like, women carry diseases and stuff, and then give them to soldiers. There's a whole history of women bringing down Armies, he said, and we should have never let them in because they just weaken the ranks."

"You can't be serious."

"That's what he said. That the Navy has the right idea—they won't even let women on their ships because they're bad luck." White laughs.

"Fuck you, man. That's not funny." I dig my fingernails into my palms. Over the blaring radio and clanging of wrenches I shout so the other mechs can hear, "I just had a kidney infection. It's not the clap, or gonorrhea, or AIDS, for fuck's sake. Now you can all stop avoiding me." I turn to White. "Is that why no one came to visit me?"

"I mean, I guess." He shrugs and looks down at his unshined boots. "Sergeant Bluff told us if we cared about our careers then we should care about appearances."

Chapter 28

Coal Dead Heart

After my death, when I'm cut open, an embalmer will find inside my hollow chest a hard chunk of coal. The pressures of military life hammer down. An eon passes in a single year. In just the last twelve months here, something soft and alive inside me died and decayed. Turning living creatures into minerals and rock took the mountains of my home millions of years, but the Army did it in one. While they have almost mined me out, I'm far from dead or inert. All that is required for an explosion is the slightest spark. Sergeant Bluff struck, setting off a blast.

Standing beside my smashed up BMW off the *Autobahn* as I watch the person I once loved drive away, I assess the damage. In just a few moments, flames have engulfed my entire life. Nothing stands now but an empty hole. I feel nothing. I am numb. I am dead inside.

Technically, I am still alive. The German drivers who have stopped to help remind me how lucky I am to have escaped with my life. They look shocked that I'm still here, but I can't imagine any other possibility. Sergeant Bluff is calling for the Army to kick me out on a bad conduct discharge, AKA a Chapter 14, for last Tuesday's "incident". Fate would not let me escape that easily.

Last week's run-in with Sergeant Bluff is the third such event in my brief career as an Active Duty soldier. The first, the "Shitbag incident", occurred last August when I was late to work. The second, the "forklift incident", involved my accidental stabbing of my forks into a German cargo truck. Despite calls for my demotion and discharge, I escaped without punishment. Perhaps it was because Sergeant Bluff knew he was in the wrong that life went back to the way it was like nothing happened.

But this one feels different. It is a disaster unmatched by any of my other so-called incidents. Last Monday, a week and a half ago, life was calm, boring. I could have never imagined the events leading to this calamity. What started as friction between Sergeant Bluff and Sergeant Ruiz and their conflicting directives ends with me standing in the middle of a firestorm.

Sergeant Bluff, as NCO in charge of the barracks, ordered those of us who live there to report for barracks maintenance immediately after final formation. As the seventeen-hundred hour formation approached, I straightened up my desk and turned off my computer. It would be a short day in the motor pool compared to the late nights and weekends I had been working. Ordered to barracks formation, I told Sergeant Ruiz I would not be back, but he said to forget about formation and come back to work. Sergeant Bluff was not my platoon sergeant. He promised he would "take care of Sergeant Bluff".

I don't know what, if anything, happened between the two men, but the next day, after our PT run, a slow trickle of soldiers, sweaty and red-faced, gathered into loose platoons on the concrete basketball court behind the barracks. Sergeant Bluff stood stiff and tall up front, the place designated for our new First Sergeant if he ever came to PT. My former platoon sergeant looked like he was auditioning for the job of our company's NCO-IC.

Hiding in the rear behind the coalescing cloud of soldiers, I chatted with Specialist James, one of the new female soldiers in the SSA. She pulled down her socks to model the tattoo of a knife dripping blood on her right calf. I asked her what it meant. She smiled and said it was a tribute to her ex who she would murder if she ever saw again. I said I'd like to get a tattoo-tribute to the Army, maybe an M-16 on my ass or perhaps a blood-soaked bayonet over my heart as a tribute to the Army.

Our laughter drowned out Sergeant Bluff as he droned on about the latest event to piss him off. He was little more than background noise until he raised his voice, claiming no one showed up for barracks maintenance the night before.

A soldier buried deep in the petroleum platoon spoke up. "We were all there," the soldier said. Standing on my toes to see who spoke, I still could not see him in the crowd.

"Not everyone," Sergeant Bluff said.

"Who wasn't there, Sergeant?"

"Lots of people," Sergeant Bluff said. "Burton, for one. Where was Burton last night?"

My eyes bulged at Sergeant Bluff tossing around my name, offering my absence as indisputable proof of my laziness. "What the fuck?" I muttered, looking around for Sergeant Ruiz or Sergeant Westen. They would set him straight, tell him I had been in the motor pool until past twenty-one hundred last night. But that morning, neither my squad leader nor my platoon sergeant was anywhere to be found.

I was on my own to defend myself. Pleading my innocence, I shouted out, "I was in the damn motor pool, Sergeant."

Sergeant Bluff's face was evidence of his growing internal turbulence. He burst out, shouting across the basketball court, "You cussing me, Burton?" His sudden rage threatened to blow me off my feet. "Who do you think you're cussing at? Get over here." He pointed in front of his toes.

I walked toward Sergeant Bluff. Meeting me halfway, he told me to accompany him to the rear. Ordered to parade rest, I put my hands behind my back, stiffened my body, and stared straight ahead. He screamed, "I said get at parade rest."

"I am at parade rest, Sergeant."

"No you're not. Get at parade rest and stop talking."

I straightened my posture and fixed my eyes straight. I tried not to look at the man who, inches from my face, peered into my irises, daring me to look back at him. My eyes darted to meet his as he moved closer.

"Who do you think you're looking at?"

I looked ahead again, saying nothing.

"Huh?" he asked. "Who are you staring at?"

"I'm not looking at no one, Sergeant."

"No one, no one? Who do you think you're talking to? What's my name? Say my name."

I gasped. I was reminded of that scene in the movie *American Pie*, in which the red-headed girl, naked with a guy in bed, punches the pillow. She shouts, "What's my name? Say my name, bitch."

I trembled with humiliation. Silently, I willed my body to stiffen.

"What's my name? Say my name."

I braced myself. "Bitch", the next word in the movie's line, hung in the air.

Sergeant Bluff, for a third time, demanded, "What's my name? Say my name."

Sweat drenched my hair, and I felt steam rise off my head. I clenched my jaw, took a pained breath, and tried to calm my shaking body.

Behind me, the female soldiers in Sergeant Bluff's platoon sucked their teeth. "Who does he think he is?" James asked. "*Say my name*? He must think he's Destiny's Child."

A fever as hot as a piece of coal in a Stoker Stove swept my forehead. In front of me, Sergeant Bluff hovered with his enormous face with his snarling teeth. A few minutes dragged into what felt like hours. I felt everyone's eyes on me. Sergeant Bluff was far from giving up. I didn't want to let him win, but I couldn't stand the embarrassment a second longer.

Looking him in the eye, I snarled, "Sergeant Bluff. *Sergeant. Bluff.*" He returned my glare, but I refused to flinch.

"That's it, Burton," he said. "I've got something for your ass. Come see me and I'll have a counseling statement waiting for your ass."

He slunk off toward the company building across the narrow street, where I ran sprints on my busted ankle. The old familiar pain shot up through my rigid ankle.

Trying to hide my shame, I kept quiet, holding my head high as I made my way back toward formation.

"What is his problem?" James asked. "Why did he single you out? You're not even in our platoon."

My cheeks burned hot as a barrel of an M-60 machine gun. The inferno raging inside me blasted through what was still standing of my walls. I didn't even try to contain the explosion. The damage was already done. I didn't care if Sergeant Bluff or even the First Sergeant might be watching from his office window of the top floor.

"Oh, Sergeant Bluff's got me now." I clapped my hands out in front of me. "It took a whole year, but he finally found something to hang me on."

Pointing my rear toward the company building, I did a swan dive. I wrapped my fingers around my calves and looked back between my knees.

"Here, Sergeant Bluff," I hollered in the direction of the Company HQ. "Let me grab my ankles, so when you fuck me up the ass it will be easier on you."

For a week, I spoke little of what happened. I waited for the unknown. Then two days ago, a week after the episode, I was ordered to report upstairs of the Company HQ Building. Sergeant Bluff was waiting in the conference room when I arrived.

Motioning to the large mahogany table that took up most of the room, he said, "Come on in, Burton. Sit down. Anywhere." I threw my body into the plush upholstered swivel chair at the head of the table. In front of me, he placed a DA Form 4856. "Here is your counseling statement," he said.

Hovering over my left shoulder, he leaned in and pointed with his middle finger to the parts of the statement he had written up. I squinted at the two small paragraphs he no doubt instructed a junior enlisted soldier to type up on an electric typewriter. He would not have done it himself. "Hardcore" soldiers from all-male MOSs would never stoop to learn a "soft skill" possessed by so-called pussy ass soldiers like me who work as supply and office clerks. Staring down at the words, the irony that the Army needs soldiers for this work yet despises them for being able to perform it, was not lost. I snorted and shook my head.

"What are you laughing at Burton?" Sergeant Bluff asked.

"Not a thing, Sergeant," I said, flipping the paper to page two on the backside.

"That second page is for you, for you to write your statement."

"Yes, Sergeant." I flipped the page back over to the front.

I read over the first page more closely. In a small single spaced paragraph under the heading "Summary of Counseling" he wrote his version of the events. In seven sentences, he made his case against me. He claimed I had cussed at him, saying I was in the "GOD DAM" motor pool. According to his misspelling of the word, he said I "roled" my eyes. He wrote he told me three times to "AT EASE", but I continued to talk, according to him, and was "breathing heavy as if you wished to strike me." Although he didn't state what they were, he said I made "bodily gestures" while "being disrespectful".

It was in the second paragraph on that same page that he recommended my removal from the Army under a Chapter 14 discharge. Sergeant Bluff wrote that under a Chapter 14, I "could experience severe prejudice in civilian life and would lose virtually all veterans benefits." I would forever be labeled a Shitbag, grouped in with other soldiers kicked out under that same Chapter 14 for deserting the military or going AWOL.

It was all my fault, according to the statement. There was, of course, no mention of his disrespect toward me. Maybe he believed a sergeant can't disrespect a lower-ranking person, but I knew better. The Army has rules about what a man, even of his rank, can say or do.

I pulled the pen from my BDU's breast pocket. Resisting the urge to stab it like a bayonet into Sergeant Bluff's heart, I placed it on the table. If I wanted to come out of this alive, if I wanted to save my life, it would be by a pen, not an M-16.

Flipping the document to its back side, I found the little box next to the words, "Individual disagrees with the information above." Beyond those words, less than a quarter of the page was allocated to my writing my side of the story.

I looked up at Sergeant Bluff. "This is not going to be enough space for all I'm going to write."

"We've got paper." His face contorted into a sneer. "We've got all the paper you want."

"Good," I said, annunciating the word short and sharp. "Because I'm writing a book. Sergeant."

Sergeant Bluff blanched. For the first time, I saw fear flashing across his face. Without a word, he walked toward the office cabinets lining the wall. When he returned, he smacked down in front of me a small stack of blank Xerox paper.

In the box next to "do not agree" I drew a large, dark X, then smiled up at him.

"That's fine," he said. "Write what you want to write. I'll leave you to it."

He walked away, and I started writing. I started with, "I do not agree with the statement."

After that, I paused to think about what to write next. I looked back at Sergeant Bluff's words. More important than what he wrote was what he did not. His sentences were vague, unspecific, and speculative. Besides twisting my words into "GOD DAM", he mentioned little else either of us had said during the "incident". Although he wrote that he had told me three times to "AT EASE", omitted was how he had ordered me that same number of times to say his name.

For the better part of an hour, I mulled over my words. From time to time, a soldier peaked in through the door at me. "Still writing," I shouted each time.

I closed my eyes and recalled the scene. As if I were a bystander, I saw over and over Sergeant Bluff shouting, "Say my name. What's my name?" I wrote it all down, everything that happened. Providing a glimpse into my feelings, I wrote I found Sergeant Bluff's orders to say his name "quite offensive". That phrase, I said, was "used to degrade a person and make ~~them~~ her feel inferior as a human being". I wrote what I said to "one of my comrades that I believed Sergeant Bluff to be biased against me" and that "he's holding a grudge since he was my NCO in the SSA and that still he would like to make things harder on me".

In my last paragraph, I left my readers, the First Sergeant and Sergeant Bluff, with something to think about. "I believe Sergeant Bluff was being disrespectful by asking me to say his name," I wrote. I ended with, "I do not believe that request to be appropriate and did not wish to degrade myself in order to give Sergeant Bluff pleasure."

Laying down my pen, I trembled. My body felt that day all over again.

Today, Thursday, marks forty-eight hours since I wrote the words I hoped would save me. I have had no news about anything. Since the showdown, since the statement, I went to formation, done PT, reported to my job in the motor pool, all while pretending nothing was wrong. After being dismissed at fifteen-hundred hours today for Thursday Family Time, I counted down the hours of free-time I would have to fret and worry. I could not pace my room like a jail cell, waiting to hear if I would hang for my accused crimes. The walls of my tiny shoebox of a room closed in. I opened a window. I was trapped. I couldn't breathe. If I didn't escape that room, those barracks, that Army base, I would suffocate. From my wall-locker I found my go-to civvies, my armor. Pulling my black pleather jacket over my pink boucle turtleneck paired with gray trousers, I felt feminine, strong.

I jumped into my car and headed for the nearest exit off base. Once the gate guards were in my rearview, I hit the gas and cranked up the stereo. The techno beat of "Blue" by Eiffel 65 wailed inside my car, my brain, my muscles. At the top of my lungs, I sang along with the auto-tuned voice of the singer as he crooned, "I'm blue, da ba dee, da ba dee..."

My arms and legs stiffened with unburned energy. I needed to release it into a force—if not a punch, then speed and power. I headed straight for the *Autobahn*. The icy rain mixed with sleet and pounded my car's windshield, but I paid no attention. I was free to drive as fast as I wanted. I needed to tempt Death, to lure him out of hiding, to face him and defeat him again. I wanted to battle Death again and show him who was boss. I stomped my foot on the gas pedal. The car quivered and my stomach jumped up into my throat like I was on a roller coaster..

"C'mon, motherfucker, let's go," I shouted over the music as I tried to redline the engine.

I came up too fast on a more cautious driver in front. Moving to the slow lane to avoid a collision with the Mercedes, my car skidded, almost sending me crashing into a pokey little hatchback. I spotted the exit for the town of Erdbeeren. Hoping to escape disaster, I directed the car off the *Autobahn* and onto the exit ramp. I couldn't burn off enough speed. Tapping the brakes, the car slid off the *Autobahn*, barreling ninety-miles an hour into the *Ausfahrt* sign.

Now, before I even unbuckle my seatbelt and get out of my car, two German drivers stop to help. The car fumes. As I open the door and step out, a motherly lady pulls at my arm, dragging me away from the BMW, which is threatening to go up in flames. The *Ausfahrt* sign, or exit sign, twisted and mangled in the middle of my hood, points down at the ground, toward hell.

Through some odd workings of the universe, my boyfriend Markus in his work van pulls up moments after the accident. He looks me over and says, "Mein Gott. Du bist so Weiss."

I put my hands to my face as if I can feel my white face. At last I am growing aware of how narrowly I escaped Death once again. I thought it was all a matter of skill, of outmaneuvering my foe, but I had not accounted for how much luck was involved.

Markus asks if I am hurt. When I say no, he tells me his boss must be wondering about his whereabouts. He is late, he says, and his boss is counting on him.

"Ja, Perfekt," I say. "Go, go to the person who really needs you."

My heart turns darker and harder than the black stone on my right middle finger. The onyx ring, Markus's gift for my twenty-first birthday in November, was not the fairytale diamond I imagined. An engagement, finding true love, I was certain would offset all the other hurt of the Army. I was naïve for believing in some dumb bullshit happily ever-after for myself.

Twisting the band off my finger, I watch as Markus drives off, leaving me alone to face whatever may happen to me now. In the movies, the girl throws her ring after the car and yells, but I'm not a girl. I'm a soldier. After pulling my faux-leather purse from the passenger side seat, I unzip it and toss the ring to the bottom.

This is not the end. I am not yet dead, but Death is no longer the fearsome stranger it once was. I look back at my car. My knees buckle and the world spins. My head throbs. Maybe it was shaken inside my skull or maybe it's the fumes. I want to collapse, but I scold myself to stand up tall. But after a year of fighting, of surviving one disaster after another, I don't know how much longer I can't keep from falling. I have lost my strength.

I have lost everything in my life. Ticking off each of my prized possessions one by one, Sergeant Bluff has made good on the promise he made in his office last year to take away everything I hold dear. My car and boyfriend are only the latest losses. I failed to hold on to my big room for Specialists. My hope for a future after the Army and my health, both gone. My name and dignity, destroyed. Every reason I had to live has been burned up into smoke.

I am a Shitbag. The best thing I could do for myself, my family, and the nation is to go home in a box with a flag draped over it, just like Sergeant Bluff said. Before the Army can kick me out, while I still have some honor, I should end it. But I can't bring myself to do what the universe did not do in Poland or in the hospital or here in this crash. Death doesn't want me, either. I am doomed to do battle forever in this life. I want to kick the car tires. I want to scream and shake my hands at the heavens. I want to close my eyes and sleep forever.

The Germans look at me as I study the damage. They mutter while studying me like a zoo animal. They wonder what I will do, if I will crack or cry, I am certain of it. I remind myself I can't do that. I can't be a woman or even a human. I have to be a soldier representing to our German host nation how strong and disciplined we are. Trained to set aside my emotions, I must be a killer, but also a survivor, I refuse to feel. Any emotions that creep up, I quickly bury deep in my stomach. I am programmed to obey, execute, operate. Pain, hurt, sorrow, fear, even love are luxuries are for those of warm flesh and blood. My heart feels as cold as a hunk of rock.

Looking at my scrap heap of a car, I recall my buddy Low's story of his accident on the Autobahn. He flipped his first car, a POS hatchback, upside down. The roof caved in, and he couldn't open the door. He escaped being turned into BMW roadkill, he claimed, by rolling down the window and crawling out. It was a miracle, I said, that he didn't die. He smiled his crooked grin and said, "This place can't kill me."

This memory of Low brings up something unexpected. My eyes water. My heart flutters back to life. I can't imagine losing him. But I have lost him. He has been gone now for as long as he was in my life. I can't forget him. He was my battle buddy, the one person I trusted and counted on. He was the brother I wished I always had. He never judged me, never saw me as a Shitbag, like everyone else, including me. Although I said I was strong, that I was used to people not being in my life, so I wouldn't miss him when he left, that turned out not to be true. Since he left, there hasn't been a day I don't feel his absence. In this moment I realize not only have I lost everything, but I have lost everyone who I cared about and cared about me.

My body heaves as if vomiting up all the feelings I have swallowed over this year, this life. My fear and loneliness come out as tears that fall into the mud. I muffle my sobs by stretching the lapel of my jacket over my mouth and nose, but I feel the German civilians stare. I wait for them to yell that I am embarrassing myself, to suck it up, that I am a Shitbag, but they don't. The German woman wraps her arms around me and speaks to me softly in German. Even though I don't know what she says, I know what she means. I put my head on her shoulder, and hug her. She hugs me back like I wished my mother would do. As the Polizei, then the tow truck, arrive on the scene, both the rain and my crying let up. The dark skies give way to a pale, shimmery gray. The sun bursts through the clouds to provide the last and only of that day's light.

As I climb up beside the German tow truck driver, I wave to the man and woman, strangers who said they would stay until they were certain everything was okay. I sniffle and hope the driver doesn't notice I have been crying like a child. I tell him I am a soldier, I live on base, and ask him to take what's left of me and my car to the *Kaserne*. Just inside the front gates of post is the soldiers' BMW graveyard. Somewhere in that junkyard rusts my buddy Low's old hatchback. My car will go to rest beside my friend's. I recall the end of Where *the Red Fern Grows*. I chuckle imagining a red fern springing up between our two cars.

"We survived," I say, wondering if Low might hear my words all the way in Texas.

He found his way out of this place, and so will I. But I can't keep doing this forever. I fear I will die in the Army, if I don't get out. Worse than dying is if I live and am kicked out on a Chapter 14. For the rest of my days I will be branded as a Shitbag. The two options of either letting the Army ship me home in a box or getting kicked out on a dishonorable discharge do not work for me. I choose a third option and that is walking out the gates, carrying in my hand a DD-214 stamped with an Honorable Discharge. I refuse to die. I refuse to believe I am a Shitbag.

Circling back in the opposite direction, the tow truck passes by the scene of the accident. The tire tracks and the dangling *Ausfahrt* sign don't tell the story of what happened. In the *Morgen*, the driver says, crews will replace the sign and sew back the grass. *Morgen*. Tomorrow. It will be almost like nothing happened. Almost. He tells me the most important thing is that

I'm alive. Most people who crash on the Autobahn, he says, don't ride home in a tow truck, they ride in an ambulance to the hospital.

"This place can't kill me," I say.

Placing my hand above my left breast, I feel my strong, beating heart.

Chapter 29

Nothing Happened

Today is another early spring day in Germany. Nothing really happened. Lots of things, bigger things perhaps than today's events, happened yesterday and the day before. Like the day a few weeks ago the new First Sergeant, an old buddy of Sergeant Bluff's, moved me back to the SSA from the motor pool. Sergeant Bluff's words to me were, "I've got you now. You're mine. There's no one here to protect you anymore." That was a big day.

Thunder crashes, my window pane rattles, and I'm shaken from my bed. Electric blue bolts of electricity tear at the inky black sky and light up my room. The thunder comes again as if Thor himself is angry at the U.S. Army for occupying Germany. I roll over, too tired to care about the politics or wars of Gods. I'm just a soldier. I do as I'm told, and I'm told I need to get up.

I struggle to pull myself out of bed these days. I don't know if it is because I am sick or because I no longer have the energy to deal with the reality of my situation. When I wake up, I tell myself I am dreaming, that it can't be true. I can't have really been transferred out of the motor pool and back into the SSA less than three months after leaving. I can't really be back in Sergeant Bluff's platoon.

At last I drag my tired ass out of bed for PT formation to face the morning still draped in darkness. Stepping onto the sidewalk outside barracks, I look up at the heavens, taunting the sky gods to give me their worst. I zip up my ARMY hoodie. It's March and the air still bites, but I can smell the world thawing, life waking up.

"First Sergeant said PT's upstairs in the attic," a blur of a soldier says as he darts past me back inside the barracks. "There's more storms coming."

Heading back inside, I do my best to look motivated as I climb the stairs leading to the attic on the fourth story. Although I am not on permanent profile, I might as well be. The doctors have diagnosed me with a constellation of disorders ranging from recurrent urinary tract infections accompanied by interstitial cystitis, lumbago, chronic upper airway disease, and Achilles tendonitis of the left ankle. Doctors refuse to believe or admit I am this ill, so they blame it on my emotions. I'm depressed or anxious. They believe why I have these issues must be a chemical imbalance. It can't be the Army's fault.

"Hustle," another guy from my company running past me up the stairs says.

"My profile says I don't have to run because I'm depressed," I say to the back of his head. He stops and turns to look at me. I laugh, "Just kidding. It's my back. No, wait, it's my ankle. I forget. I'll have to look at my profile." He glances at me, confused, then turns and runs up the stairs.

Upstairs I join the others from my company who have already gathered. The ceiling pitches in the center and slopes all the way to the floor at the far reaches of the room. Other companies on base use their attic space in their barracks for rec rooms and outfit them with pool tables, TVs, and couches. My comrades from my own company have told me that at one time we had used this space for a rec room, but it had been converted to storage. Those living on the third floor swear the old attic is haunted and they hear footsteps above them as they try to sleep at night.

A few months ago, Sergeant Bluff, who is in the NCO in charge of the barracks, had us clean this whole space out. His plan, he said, was to convert the attic to open-bay sleeping quarters for the huge influx of new privates he expected would soon join our company. We were ordered to move a pool table with a broken leg, a leather sofa with the stuffing coming out of the cushions, even a six-foot Christmas tree still assembled with its tinsel and ornaments hanging from its branches down four flights of stairs. Knowing the stuff was headed for the trash, my comrades smashed ornaments, ripped the tree apart, and broke the cue sticks in half. In the negative, empty space we vacuumed up and dusted away any traces of old ghosts to make way for the new, the young.

As our company crowds into the now empty loft, lining all four walls and crouching under the low ceiling, soldiers find their platoons and clump together in groups instead of formations. Scanning the room for our new First Sergeant, I see no signs of him. I have rarely seen him since he took over for First Sergeant Dean who went to a new duty station in the States a few weeks ago. The company mourns First Sergeant Dean's departure as if he passed away. No one, I am certain, feels his absence more than me.

First Sergeant Dean never stated outright why he agreed to move me to the motor pool. Although I was qualified, so were other soldiers. But a few months ago I ran into him at the clinic. He was getting his exit physical, and I was there for my back or my ankle or my kidneys or my dizziness. He plopped down into the seat next to me and started talking.

"Burton," he said. I didn't think he even knew my name. "I tried to do right by my soldiers. I tried to protect you, but I'm leaving now and there's nothing more I can do." He looked straight ahead as he spoke. "But this new first sergeant... He's Sergeant Bluff's buddy from Stateside. You soldiers will have to look out for each other now."

Today in the attic, Sergeant Bluff finds his place at the front of his platoon cluster. He inhales, broadening his chest. He raises his chin and lowers his eyes to survey us. Beyond his head, just through the window, the sky blues with flashes of lightning while thunder claps. He smiles as if he's commanded the heavens to time their sound effects to his arrival.

In his left hand he grips a stack of manila folders. He narrows his eyes and purses his lips into a smirk. He nods, and a snort of laughter escapes through his nose. He calls us to attention, then puts us at ease. "Look at you." He wears a look of equal parts disgust and hurt. "You're a disgrace to the Army." Lowering my head, I sneak a peek to my left and right. In the last row of the four-rank formation, I fold the shoulders of my five-foot-four frame forward until they almost meet over my flat chest. "You know who I'm talking to. I'm talking to the ones whose files I got right here." He waves the folders at the sky as if he might cue the thunder and lightning. "I'm talking to those soldiers who can't pass a PT test, who ride profile."

"Shitbags," someone behind me pretends to cough. Laughter rumbles through the ranks and Sergeant Bluff smiles.

"Raise your hand if you're on profile," he pauses. "And raise your hand if you failed your last PT test. It will be one and the same for some of you." He grins and a couple guys behind me laugh. Keeping my hand lowered, I look around at the soldiers beside me. No one raises their hand.

"I didn't expect any of you Shitbags to have any integrity. You know what?" He looks at the tab on the first manila folder, then flips it open. "You can just bring your asses up to the front of the formation and let the platoon have a good look at you. When I call your name, come up here and get your damn file." One by one, he reads the names and the PT scores of at least half a dozen soldiers out of about twenty in the platoon.

Holding my breath, I wait until at last he calls out, "Burton," and reads to the platoon the totals for my push-ups, sit-ups, and my runtime on my last PT test. I walk toward the front and take my folder. Looking him in the eyes, I say, "It's a passing score, Sergeant. I passed my PT test, you know that." He ignores the comment. It doesn't matter that I passed, I'm on profile. He reads the name and scores of the next file. I take my place among those standing in front of the formation.

Feeling exposed in my flimsy gray PT sweats and without my Battle Dress Uniform, boots, or even cap to disguise my flaming red hair under the fluorescent lights, I smile at my accusers. They stare back with narrow, hateful eyes. I get the feeling they would like to build a stake and light it right where we—*I*—stand.

"Look up here." Sergeant Bluff gestures toward us while addressing his platoon. "Everyone you see standing up here is a Shitbag. They don't even deserve to be called soldiers. They don't care about you, their comrades. They leave you to do all the work while they run off to sick-call to get profiles. They're just trying to get this over with and their PT scores show it."

"Hooah," PFC Landry calls out from behind another guy. His neck cranes around the shorter soldier in front of him so we can all see his bright, yellow teeth glowing up at Sergeant Bluff. "They're shammers, Sergeant." Biting my tongue until I'm sure I taste blood, I hold back from asking Sergeant Bluff when he plans to announce our ASVAB test scores. Landry admitted to having to take the test twice just to score high enough to enlist.

"I'm going to put them out," Sergeant Bluff announces. "We don't need people like these in our ranks. I don't want people like these in my Army."

He'd be saving me the work of convincing the doctors I deserve out on a medical. My body, even my brain, is little more than a used and useless vesicle. I'm tired of fighting for my rank. I'm tired of fighting for my place here. I'm tired of fighting. I want out before he picks off what remains of me like he did to Dale and Dix.

One night, in an attempt to recapture something of our former selves, Dale, Dix, and I went out dancing and drinking until the early morning. In formation a couple of hours later, we smelled of sweat, vodka, and the good ole days. Someone had to pay, and Sergeant Bluff chose Dale. He was busted from Specialist E-4 all the way down to Private E-1.

Not long after that, Dix got caught with his cock out at the wrong time with the wrong person. He was hustled out of the barracks under the cover of darkness, without a goodbye to anyone. In the morning a few of us went up to his room, pushed open the unlocked door and found it empty, as if he never existed.

"They should have never been in here to begin with, but until I can fix what Basic Training failed to do," Sergeant Bluff gestures toward those of us standing in the front, "I'm going to need you all to step up and take some initiative."

A collective, "Hooah," pours forth from the platoon.

I glance over to see PFC Romero standing to my right. We haven't spoken since that conversation we had before Christmas—about reporting Sergeant Bluff to the IG. Her foot is no longer bandaged, but she was limping when she walked up here. She grunts, jutting out her hip and shifting her weight to her right foot.

To my left stands Private Abela, a brand-new soldier to the

platoon. With his lean runner's body and closely sheared hair, he looks like he's still a recruit, just out of high school. During PT, I've never seen him walk or do any other modified exercise. He's a fast runner, so I puzzle over why he's up front with the rest of us. Rumors swirl he's gay. Thanks to Don't Ask, Don't Tell, our superiors cannot force Abela, or anyone else, to discuss his sexuality. However, there's no protection from other soldiers who might take offense with their comrades' private lives.

"It's either you or them," Sergeant Bluff nods in our direction. "People like this will get you killed when you go down range. They're not going to have your back in a foxhole. They'll be worried about themselves."

"Hooah," the soldiers in front of us roar. "Buddy-fuckers."

"That's right." He beams a proud papa smile at his shouting troops. "I was in the Persian Gulf and we had a way of taking care of soldiers like these. It was a little thing called friendly fire."

The crowd erupts. I look around at the other platoons and their platoon sergeants. I wait for them to intervene, to speak up. The sergeant from the petroleum and oil platoon makes eye contact. Silently I plead with him to stop this. He opens his mouth, then turns his head back to his own soldiers like nothing happened.

"We don't have the luxury of a war right now so you all have to get creative," Sergeant Bluff continues. "I can't tell you what to do, but you can think of something. You know their habits—you live with them in the barracks." He pauses, smiles. The soldiers standing with me stare straight ahead with numb, expressionless faces. Inside I'm shouting my disbelief and I can't imagine my face registers anything but shock. "You shower with them, you eat chow with them. There are dark places on this base where no one sees. Come talk to me after formation. I can tell you where those places are."

"Yeah, that's right, Sergeant," some disembodied male voice from the platoon calls out.

Encouraged, Sergeant Bluff smiles, "And I'm in charge of the barracks. There's a second set of keys to every room in the Company Building. Like I said... Come see me after formation."

"Hooah," the platoon pulses. I shut my eyes as I anticipate the storm surge. The electricity crackles inside the dry room. My scalp tingles and the hairs on my arms stand on end. "Goddamn Shitbags."

As the sky darkens that evening, stillness descends over the barracks. The thunder and lightning of the early morning is replaced by the sun in time for it to set. There's a quiet that could be mistaken for the exhaustion after a disaster, but it's the calm before the storm.

Locking the door behind me as I enter my room, I wonder if there's any use. There's no furniture to put under the door, there's no squeezing my hundred-and-fifteen-pound body through the opening of the window and jumping to the concrete below; there's nothing to do but sit on my bed and wait.

All night, I will keep a vigilant guard duty. I will not leave my post, not even to go to the latrine. My uniform is my BDUs and boots. There will be no sleep. From its pouch on my right hip, I remove my Gerber utility knife and place it beside me. The TV is turned down low enough to provide company, but not loud enough that someone in the hallway might think I'm here. In my lap I open a notebook and write the date and a brief paragraph of today's events. I can't bring myself to recount the gory details of my shame. In between nodding off and staring at the door, I read a book to break the monotony. From time to time my body cries out for me to pay attention to the parts of it that ache and spasm and burn. I pop more Ibuprofen horse pills, drink another Coke, and count down the hours until the night fades into morning.

I drift off into that stage between wakefulness and sleep when thoughts become dreams or dreams become thoughts. Scenes of my Army life with me in the starring role replay like movie trailers. I see the highlights, the action scenes, the clips of dialogue between me and other soldiers, villains and friends alike.

I see drill sergeants yelling, "What makes the green grass grow," and me with a bayonet at the end of my rifle yelling back in response, "Blood, blood, bright red blood." I sink my bayonet into the green Styrofoam torso on the obstacle course. At seventeen, I've just glimpsed behind the curtain of the adult world. On the bayonet course, I marvel at how good it feels to let my anger pour through the tip of the blade.

My English professor appears after that. We are standing in the classroom after he has rearranged the furniture so he can see all entrances and exits. He asks me why I want to go to the Army full time. My short answer, to see the world, must seem dumb and naïve to a Vietnam War veteran. He warns me that the Army will use me for all they can get and throw me away.

Sergeant Bluff shows up next, standing before my two buddies and me in the warehouse. He's there, again telling us how we should just die in the Army, that no one wants us, that we're disposable. He's saying we were fools for thinking we enlisted for some higher purpose; we agreed to give our lives so powerful men can use us for their own, selfish purposes.

Finally I see myself in the woods in Poland, running, exhausted and wheezing. Someone, a dark figure, closes in on me. When I realize I will never outrun this monster, I recall my hand-to-hand combat training in Basic. With no rounds and no bayonet, my only option is to draw back and hit the creature with the butt of my weapon. I mean to come home alive.

"Kill, kill, kill." The words are on my lips as I bolt upright. There's the sound of metal clanging. I try to kick off my sleeping bag; I search for my M-16. I won't lie silent in my bed and hope he passes over me, not this time. My hand grabs my Gerber and I realize I'm in my bed, not back in Poland in my cot. For a second I let relief rush over me; I'm not in the field. Then I realize why I'm gripping my utility knife, why I'm sitting in my uniform, and why my feet are swelling inside my boots in the middle of the night.

The heavy walnut door clangs on its hinges and the brass handle shakes, jolting me from my past into my present reality. In one fluid motion, I flip open the blade of the Gerber and jump to my feet. I cross the room and stare at the door. It quivers inside its frame as if it might come loose. I stand in front of it, ready for the storm of troops to burst in. Then the room and the door go silent.

I place my hand flat against the door and stare at the hinges, wondering if it has held off the invaders. Through the cracks, I hear baritone whispers laughing and conspiring in the hallway. The handle jiggles again and I jump back, remembering the set of keys Sergeant Bluff promised to procure for his soldiers. I feel sick. I don't know if I have the strength to face what might come through that door. I think of lying in a pool of vomit and letting them do what they will, but that terrifies me more than fighting back.

"Fix bayonets." A former drill sergeant's words spill out of my brain and into my body. I remember that night in Poland in the woods when I could no longer run, raising my M-16 to fight. I call on my muscles as well as my hippocampus for the memories. Steadying my hand and my breathing, I point the blade out in front of me. My fear disappears and I crave violence. I want to see the surprise and pain on each of their faces as I thrust the blade between their ribs. In their last moments they will recognize the error of swearing to defend a man who wraps himself up in the flag instead of the constitution they promised to defend. Some will go back wounded to their demagogue. At last they will see a different version of the story, the one I've written. One that does not end with my death.

The door shivers, the handle flies up, the voices penetrate the barrier, the nerves of my body spark and crackle. Then as if the barracks were holding its breath, now it exhales and relaxes. The door sinks back into its jamb, the handle falls down into place, and footsteps carry the voices away down the hall, leaving only whispers and sighs of relief.

Falling back onto my bed with my Gerber still open, I stare out at the nothingness, listening to the silence. Perhaps it was just a dream. Maybe it was a product of too much Ibuprofen and antibiotics and too little sleep. Perhaps it was the last remnants of the storm, blowing through the hallways shaking my door, howling through the cracks of the old wooden frame. Maybe it was the ghosts floating in white sheets from the attic, rattling chains and doors on the first floor.

"Nothing happened," I whisper.

My buddy Low, like a ghost, speaks to me. "The Army is just a game and we're players in it. You've got to learn to play their game," he says, and I remember now. Despite Sergeant Bluff's calls for me to hand over the duplicate set, I kept putting him off until tomorrow, then tomorrow. I pull out my nightstand drawer and find the two sets of keys to my barracks room.

CHAPTER 30

SPOILED

Sergeant Bluff scrunches up his face and smacks his lips like he's caught a whiff of some foul smell in his office. "Spoiled," he says, surveying his platoon, which he has called into his office.

The word conjures up memories of my childhood and running barefoot in the hot, sticky summer months with my cousins and brother—through the grove of apple trees in Mamaw's yard up our holler in Stinking Creek. Somehow we knew, as if by instinct, how to avoid the sweet, firm fruit that fell to the ground and threatened to hobble us during our games of tag or hide and seek. However, the soft, rotten apples burrowed into the ground, hiding and waiting to squish up between our toes and release their sour, decaying smell. We laughed at the cool, soft, mushy feeling and wiped the spoiled apples off our feet in the tender grass under the trees.

How far away that life of long summers in Kentucky feels now. Bavaria's spring outside Sergeant Bluff's windows tries to break the cool, tenacious winter, but every morning a frost lays itself across the ground.

"You're all a bunch of spoiled, lazy, undisciplined soldiers,"

Sergeant Bluff says, droplets of spit dripping onto his desk. "Do you know why I've called you all in here?"

I look around at the dozen or so soldiers lined up around the room to see what we might have in common. It's almost the entire platoon, all lower-enlisted soldiers. As a Specialist I outrank almost everyone here. After almost a year and a half in, I've been here longer than almost anyone else.

When, how did I become the longest-serving, highest ranking non-NCO? How was I not dead three, four times over? How was I not kicked out on my ass with a bad conduct discharge? I somehow managed to write my way out of every threat of a demotion and bad discharge. With skill, some help, and just plain dumb luck, I am still alive. I have stayed long enough to watch many of my fellow soldiers leave. Some I liked like Dale and Dix. Others, like Low, I loved. Many like Lemske, Peterson, and Horne I am glad are gone.

The soldiers here now, almost all of them Privates and PFCs, have arrived straight from Basic and AIT in the States. At twenty-one, and having completed Basic Training in the last millennium, I feel like an old-timer. The new folks all bond over their Basic done at Ft. Jackson. Some already know each other from their time together at AIT and are quick to become friends

They talk about recent movies, like *Pearl Harbor*, which I've only seen dubbed into German. Looking around at this new crop of soldiers, only one thing seems to unite most of us and that's our gender. Except for three or four guys, we're all women. Our platoon is almost entirely female, which I never noticed until now. I smile; my chest warms and I feel like we've just scored some victory.

"You all have had it too good in here. You don't know how good you've had it. I'm about to show you how good you've had it," Sergeant Bluff says.

My brain and my body feel numb and dumb from hearing all

this before. I don't fear the threats anymore like I used to. When I first arrived, I had so much to lose. I was scared what would happen if Sergeant Bluff followed through on his threats to take my car, my boyfriend, my nice, large room, my career.

I imagined, once, that it would devastate me to lose everything I came into the Army to find, everything I had worked so hard for, everything I had ever desired. I wondered once if I lost those things if I could even go on.

Instead, there is a certain freedom in losing it all. Nothing holds me to this place, to this life. A soldier needs only what she can carry and carries only what she needs. Sergeant Bluff has nothing with which to threaten me. He is not my daddy. I have no father. I have no mother. Uncle Sam has turned his back on his niece. I am a twenty-one-year-old woman and I belong to no one.

Looking around the room, I notice the younger, more tender soldiers wilting under Sergeant Bluff's intense heat. Their shoulders slump and their heads droop toward the floor. Most have been here no longer than a few months. I wonder how many, like me, will barely make it through to the next season.

"You're all weak-minded." Sergeant Bluff leans forward in his squeaky metal chair, rolling it on its casters closer to the heavy wooden desk. "I got most of my platoon on some kind of profile." I recognized a lot of the soldiers from the day he brought us to the front of the formation for being hurt. "A weak body is a sign of a weak mind. This shit never happened when I was in charge of the infantry. This is what happens when the Army puts me in charge of a bunch of females."

The few men in the room shift their weight from foot to foot. They huff and roll their eyes. They shoot me and some other women dirty looks.

Sergeant Bluff sits up straight in his chair. "Females ain't got no place in my Army." He clasps his hands and leans back. "You all need to go back to the WACS. Go back to the days when you were secretaries in your own Army, go back to where you belong. You're weakening the real Army." He shifts forward in his seat again and stairs out at us. "You don't belong in my Army. And I won't stop until I put every one of you females out."

A couple of snickers rumble from the crowd. Across the room a small group of guys pretend to stifle their laughs. They look up at me, giggling. As I narrow my eyes at them, they continue to snicker. Then I survey the room, watching the handful of men look at each of us women, who now outnumber the male soldiers three or four to one.

I feel for the Gerber on my hip. I have come close to using it on some so-called brave young men. In Poland I learned I can kill, kill, kill without mercy if I have to. I can be the cold-hearted killer who has no regard for human life. I have never told anyone that a rage now burns inside me thanks to my time in Poland. Nor have I ever spoken of what happened in the barracks. The shame of being a soldier, yet someone's target, keeps me quiet. Now I wonder who else among me has come close to using her Gerber and has never said a word.

"Who wants to be first?" I turn my head toward Sergeant Bluff's voice, his smirking face. "Which one of you females wants to be the first one out of my Army? I'll start the paperwork today. C'mon. Raise your hand."

Jerking my hand in the air, I say, "Me, Sergeant. I'll be first." I grin. "Choose me, please." There's almost a collective gasp from the others. They must think I'm a crazy person or someone with a death wish, but I know Low would be proud of the smart ass I've become. The other women stare, wide-eyed, but I look back. If Sergeant Bluff put every female soldier out of his platoon, he wouldn't have an Army. There would be one, maybe two, soldiers left in each section. The invisible machinery of logistics that keeps the military fed, armed, clothed, and even sheltered would grind to a halt.

We lock eyes and what goes unsaid passes between us for what feels like all eternity. This time I don't blink, I don't look away. My eyes and mind are focused and clear for the first time in months. His brown eyes are cloudy and bloodshot, but in them it's clear he knows even if no one else will ever believe me, I know everything.

"Put your hand down, Burton," he says with calm measure. "You ain't going nowhere."

The Army could give me a medical discharge since I can no longer run or march on my busted ankle, and especially since my stint in the hospital. I am exhausted from the recurrent bouts of bronchitis and urinary tract infections. My body never seems to heal. Sergeant Bluff could encourage my commander to sign off on the paperwork. However, he insists I stay in and under his command. He needs an enemy to rally his troops against. I can be the face of that enemy.

Looking around, he says, "Things are going to change around here."

Things have already changed around here. His office is sloppier than ever, with piles of papers on the desk and enough dust on the pictures to make the back of the warehouse look clean. Perhaps with Peterson gone, he really has lost his maid and secretary. Maybe I owe her an apology. Maybe she wasn't a buddy fucker, but was taking one for the team all along.

"You think things were so horrible that you had to go and call the IG on me?"

My ears perk up. He found out someone called the Inspector General. So that's what this is about. I know someone reported him, but I don't know who. My new squad leader, Sergeant Donahue, who was my comrade before getting promoted to Sergeant, approached me a few days ago about giving a statement.

"We need your help," Sergeant Donahue said in quiet whispers. I stopped slicing open a box to look at him. "We need you to give an interview to the IG, tell him about the stuff Sergeant Bluff's done."

"No." I shook my head and went back to my task. "Hell, no. The IG interviewed us all the last time, but what happened? Nothing."

"This time will be different," he said. "We've got a whole bunch of soldiers willing to give statements. I'm even going to talk to him about when I was still a Specialist."

"You're giving a statement?" I put the boxcutters down and glared at him.

He smiled.

"And you're sure that all these other soldiers aren't going to ass out and change their stories when Sergeant Bluff threatens them, just like before?"

"No," he said. "Not this time. These new soldiers, they're not going to do that. They're not Lemske and Peterson or even Horne. Plus this time we're going to make sure he interviews us in private instead of as a group, like the last time. No one will know what you say."

"I'm not doing it. I don't give a fuck about anything or anyone anymore."

"Burton," he said. "That's not true."

"Yeah, it is. I'm done. I've tried to tell people about him, but look what happens. I just get more shit for it. I'm going to worry about myself. Fuck everyone else."

He gave me a wounded look.

"I'm focusing on getting out of here. I've had enough. All I want is my DD214 giving me my honorable discharge for medical reasons. I'm not jeopardizing that by talking to some IG."

"How would it jeopardize that?"

"Do you know how many times Sergeant Bluff has threatened

to kick me out with a dishonorable discharge? If he finds out I spoke to an IG..."

"He won't find out."

"He always finds out about everything." I crossed my arms and looked away. "Besides, why should I care? No one ever gave a shit about me when I asked for help. Everyone looked away. These soldiers are not my friends, hell, they're not even my comrades. Everyone in here says that I'm just faking my injuries because I'm some Shitbag who doesn't want to work. Let them know what it is like to be labeled a Shitbag by Sergeant Bluff."

"That's not true, Burton," Sergeant Donahue said. "These soldiers are not Sergeant Bluff's soldiers. They aren't Lemske and Peterson. Think about what you went through. You don't really want that to happen to anyone else. I promise these soldiers are different. We're all a team now. We're going to work together."

Glancing around Sergeant Bluff's little room, I try to figure out who might have reported him. A few angry men eyeball me. Hoping to further piss them off, I shoot them a smirky grin. I scrutinize the body language of each of my comrades. Romero is staring down at her feet, picking at her hands. She must have followed through on her threats to call the IG. Good for her, I laugh.

"What are you laughing at, Burton?" Sergeant Bluff asks. I shake my head, and he picks up where he left off. "Nothing's going to happen to me, but shit's going to happen to you all. There's nothing you or an IG can do to me. I have too much rank. It would take an act of Congress to demote me. I can do anything I want and the Army turns a blind eye to it."

It feels like a boot coming down on my head. He is right, I think. There have been so many times that people in charge have seen what Sergeant Bluff does, but they choose to look away. They choose not to believe me and others and they choose not to believe their own eyes. They see what they want to see because it serves their purposes.

"PFC Wright," Sergeant Bluff calls out. A young, eager male soldier standing in front of the file cabinet looks alert. "Reach up behind you there and hand me that something I always keep in my office." Wright puts his hands on the faded photograph of Sergeant Bluff smiling, standing proud in front of an all-male platoon of soldiers. He looks younger, happier in that picture than he does now. I wonder if he chose this photo to display because it was the happiest time of his life. A life, an Army before this one when he led men into battle, not supply specialists into his office. "Not the picture. I want what's behind it." Wright withdraws something from behind the photo. I crane my neck to see what he has. "That's it, bring it over here."

Wright lets what looks like a pint of brown liquor land with a thud on Sergeant Bluff's desk. "Whoa, careful with that." Our NCO grins at the bottle. He turns it in his hand, holding it up to the light before unscrewing the lid. He takes a whiff and closes his eyes.

His lips curl into a smile. "I'm going to have a little Hennessy and Coke." He takes a coffee mug from on top of a pile of papers. From one of his desk drawers he brings out a small bottle of Coke. The bottle gasps as it releases its gasses, then he splashes the pop into the mug. The cognac gurgles as he pours a bit, then just a little more to top it off. He turns the mug up to his lips and gulps, then sets it back down. "Ahh," he smiles as we watch the performance. "You see? I can do anything I want. The Army doesn't care because I get shit done. I accomplish the mission."

Soldiers around the room shake their heads. Many have stopped watching the spectacle.

"No one cares what happens to you. You're disposable. If I have to lose a few of you to get the mission done, even in peacetime, so what? The Army writes it off as an accident or suicide. There's no investigation into that. So go ahead and talk to the IG about me, see what happens to you."

The soldiers' complexions turn green and yellow and brown. They were wilting, withering, and wasting away. These soldiers came here full of enthusiasm and youth and strength. I wonder if I looked like that a little over a year ago. I look ahead to a year from now and wonder how many of these soldiers will be standing where I am now. I wonder how many will even survive. He will break them, not because they are weak women, but because he is a man with power.

He cackles. "I love the Army. Where else can a man like me with a double GED come in here and tell you spoiled little college kids what to do?" He looks at me. I feel the other soldiers' eyes on me.

I look at Romero. She bites her lip and stares at the floor. Her weight shifts to that one foot, her right foot, as usual. She catches me looking and peeks up at me from under heavy lids. Her eyes are bloodshot. I nod. I close my eyes and push the longing to get back to those warm, unspoiled barefoot days in Kentucky out of my thoughts.

My mind returns to Germany. Looking at Sergeant Bluff, I wonder what made him the man he is. In a little over a year, I feel I have lost my regard for human suffering. I am close to going over an edge that I might not return from. If I let myself fall, will I become like Sergeant Bluff, Sergeant Samuels, and every other asshole like them I have met in here? I told myself I would never let the Army change me. What I am now—a cold, detached, at times unfeeling machine—I once vowed to never become. But it happened, perhaps because I didn't try hard enough to stop it, or because it was necessary to survive. I can't let myself die inside. And I can't watch the same happen to these soldiers. Maybe

Sergeant Donahue is right, and if we bind together, we can put an end to what once seemed an inevitable, repeating cycle.

At last I understand what I need to do. I know now that I need to be a team player, but not the kind Sergeant Bluff had in mind.

CHAPTER 31

DÉJÀ VU

The place: a dead end holler called Stinking Creek.

The character: a little girl, still in braids, who may or may not be the victim of her own overactive imagination.

The year: irrelevant.

It was a time when America would get those foreign bastards who threatened our freedom and way of life. We had a strong president who promised to make poor people better off by helping the rich. The year was 1985. Or was it 2001? It might have even been 1956 or 1973. In a place like Stinking Creek, where the outside world fails to encroach, the year isn't marked by calendars so much as it's marked by natural and political events.

"That was the year the flood came up to the back porch, and they had to close the floodgates in town," an old aunt might say, or a farmer might say, "I reckon that might finally be the last frost of the season. Hopefully, we won't have another late winter this year." People who pass the evenings watching the news might say, "Lord help us if we got another one of them Democrats back in office. I swear, they want to ruin this country. Tax a working man plumb to death."

But to me as a little girl, the days were marked by the rising and setting of the sun, the seasons marked by changing weather. A change in time was marked by the adults' changing behavior. Flowering plants and trees like daffodils and dogwoods marked warmer days ahead; grandparents hung plastic eggs from bushes starting to burst out in yellow.

Life was slow, predictable, unchanging, and usually comforting. But sometimes the very nature of its predictability was what made it seem like one was living in the *Twilight Zone*. It might be easy for a kid who liked to play pretend and watch spooky movies to imagine that time flowed both frontwards and backwards, folding onto itself again and again. It would be impossible to know. One had to ask, and take the word of, another person that time did indeed march forward in one direction, no matter how imperceptible or contrary it might feel.

One day, not unlike many others in Stinking Creek, when I was still very young, in kindergarten, or maybe first grade, I was first confronted with the feeling that the universe wasn't exactly how I had been told it was. My mind was still open to possibility, and the world held so much wonder. My bucolic surroundings needed exploring, and I looked forward to what magic they still offered.

Not long after the Easter flowers had blossomed, darting every hillside with canary-yellow trumpet-shaped blooms, with sprigs of fresh green grass sprouting from the damp ground, I ran around my grandparents' place looking for four-leaf clovers on the cold ground. The sky was crystal clear, and the air was warm enough to mislead a child into believing she could at last run barefoot after the long winter.

Overcome by the anticipation of playing outside for the first time in months without being bundled up, I let my excitement overrule my judgment. I hadn't yet figured out that the ground temperature would take weeks, or even months, before it reached the warmth of the spring air. I threw open the screen door of Mamaw's porch, leaving my shoes inside. I ran across the wooden planks of the porch of her old white farmhouse built when my mom was a girl. My feet hit the concrete of her sidewalk, the only concrete in this whole holler, a necessary splurge for Papaw who had lost his left leg at eighteen due to a timbering accident.

I ran through Mamaw's wrought-iron gate with the elaborate trellis. My feet barely touched the narrow blacktop road that bisected the land where my grandparents' house sat and their hillside property where Mom had put our trailer when she left my father.

Nothing was stopping me from my ultimate destination, my ultimate goal of running wild and shoe-free in the mountains behind our trailer. That was until my feet sunk into the icy mud hidden beneath the green grass. If the previous man-made materials of the porch, sidewalk, and road had indicated to me the actual cold of the ground, I had failed to notice it until now. The sting sent shockwaves through the soles of my feet and up into my tailbone.

And in that instant, in the deepest part of my spine, a shiver began as I felt another sensation. It was an emotion wrapped up in physical sensations. It was foreign to me, and I had no words to describe it. But I sat in the moment, wanting to explore it, to see where it took me.

I was gasping for air. As if compelled to plop my butt on to the muddy ground my eyes grew wide. I whispered, "I had a feeling I would sit down." And I knew next that I would raise my right arm and look at it, to try to make sense of it in the world, and I would have no more control over that than I did over my dirtying the seat of my pants.

I stared off at nothing and absorbed this odd sensation. I breathed and tried to catch my breath. I said, "I have been here before."

Not only had I been in this place, but I had been in this moment.

My head ached, and the bright greens and yellows washed out into grays and whites until I couldn't make them out anymore. I wondered if I, too, was fading from existence—if anyone could still see me. I began to believe, and even fear, that I didn't exist. That I was not real. I was simply a memory that lived in the brain of a twenty-year-old, maybe even a forty-year-old, me in the distant future.

Chills ran down my body and I shook them off. I got up. I had to tell someone about my weird feeling. But I couldn't tell Mamaw. She never had the patience for what she considered the trivialities of children's lives. But Mom listened, if only because she found the games my brother and I made up funny.

After what felt like years, but was really only a few minutes, I peeled myself out of the mud and ran up the hill to our trailer. Mom, with her thick shag of chestnut hair hanging over her head, was bent over our outdated avocado green stove, trying to light a burner. A pot of water and a carton of eggs sat nearby, indicating what I hoped were preparations for Easter and not some meal of boiled eggs—the only thing Mom would make that we could afford and I would eat that wasn't cold cereal or frozen chicken. But since I had not yet developed any real concept of time, neither of day nor year, I decided not to ask and instead stick to what I came to talk about.

"Mom," I said, trying to wrap my arms all the way around the soft curves of her waist, "something weird happened to me."

She finished lighting the burner and peeled my hands off of her. "Get off me before you make me burn down the house."

"I was running up the hill," I said, stepping back to look up at her, "and it felt like I'd done it before."

"You have done it before. A lot." She turned her attention towards the dishes in the sink.

"No," I said, trying to make her listen to my amazing story of a journey through a fifth dimension. "It was weird. It didn't feel *real*."

She let out a loud sigh.

"Mom," I said, "how do you know what's real or not?"

"What are you talking about?" She looked at me, rolled her eyes, and sighed again. "I thought you were old enough to know the difference between make-believe and reality."

"No. I know that movies and TV and stuff ain't real," I continued, "but I felt like I had seen all this before. In my mind or something. What if this ain't real? What if I'm not real? What if I'm just a memory?"

She threw her head back and laughed. "Oh, my God. I'm going to have to stop letting you watch *The Twilight Zone* with me. It's affecting your brain."

"Noooo." I pouted up at her. "Mom... C'mon."

She looked back at me. "Are *you* being for real right now?"

"Yes, I'm being *for real*. How do you know?"

She sighed again and said, "You had something called déjà vu. Everyone feels it now and then."

I rolled the odd word around in my mouth. I tried to pronounce it, but failed. I asked, "What's that?"

She searched the ceiling for an answer. "It's when you have the feeling that you've done something before. Like you felt."

"Well, how do you know you haven't done that before?" I asked. "I don't know how you know for sure. How do you know what is real?"

Mom was good about entertaining my questions far beyond the point that Mamaw and Papaw would have told me I was blaspheming against God and whooped me with a switch. Maybe she enjoyed talking about such things that she had been forbidden to talk about. Maybe she was worried about her child's mental health and thought if she gave me an answer regarding reality it would stave off insanity.

"All right. Say, if you see that dog outside," she said, pointing outside the tiny window above the sink to nothing in particular, "and your papaw sees that dog outside, and your mamaw sees that same dog outside, then you can be pretty sure there's a dog outside."

I looked up into her eyes, "So what if everyone else sees a dog, but I don't? Who's right?"

Mom stared up at the ceiling again and scrunched her shoulders to her ears. "You can probably assume they are," she said.

"So I'm wrong?" I shook my head and crossed my arms. "Why are they right and I'm wrong?"

"Look." Her shoulders slumped forward and she let out a long breath. "If you're the only one who sees or hears or feels something, then you have to ask yourself why you're the only one. Basically, the way someone knows what's real is that a whole bunch of people agree it's real."

CHAPTER 32

FIGMENT OF MY REALITY

It is if I am not really here. I am not here in Germany or in the Army. It is not July. My career in the military is not coming to a halt eighteen months into my first four-year enlistment. I am in the future or the past. I am the figment of my little girl's imagination. I am the memory of my future forty-year-old self. I am the "girl-soldier" character in some book. My book.

Playing out before my eyes as I stare out into the warehouse bay is a familiar scene from my childhood. I see myself, as a little girl, running off Mamaw's porch and across our holler's winding road. In the spring mud of the hillside of my family's property, I sit among daffodils looking out at nothing.

Then in an instant, another scene appears. I am a middle-aged woman sitting next to a man I presume to be my husband. In my lap I have a notebook. Looking down, I read from the page. Laughing I tell him this is a story of my battle buddies and me in Germany. I can't believe it has been twenty years already, I say. I can't believe we survived. I can't believe I am still alive.

I shiver and wonder where I am—if I have stepped through some wormhole. My past and future are compressed to moments through which I have traveled at lightspeed. Now I slam to a stop. Everything is a memory, something I read in a book with a winding story that never ends. Then without warning the journey stops. I turn the page and read the words, THE END. So it goes in stories, as well as real life.

Sergeant Bennett's story ends with a handsome prince she met in the next kingdom. Other soldiers tell most of her tale. They say they have seen her, hair disheveled and clothes rumpled, sneaking back into our barracks in the wee hours of the spring morning. A few guys next door at 316th said they spotted her leaving the room of a certain mechanic, a sergeant, those same mornings.

Then I saw it for myself. Sergeant Bennett showed up to formation one day, without a word, wearing maternity BDUs. We had no idea. I wonder if she had any idea her handsome prince was really a toad with a wife and kids tucked away back in the States. Both their careers were in shambles. The Army was threatening to discharge Sergeant Bennett for not designating a caregiver for her baby. Her lover, too, was facing discharge for adultery.

I knew this already by the time she asked me to drive her to a prenatal appointment. She told me how no one believed her when she said that her morning sickness was more like all-day sickness and had continued into her second trimester. Despite the fact she had lost weight due to the incessant vomiting, she said Sergeant Bluff had accused her of faking. She yelled, saying her morning sickness was real. I said nothing. Why she thought I would give her sympathy after what she had done was beyond me.

She put her hand to her mouth and urged me to pull off to the shoulder. In the drizzle, and in the mud, she knelt, sobbing and dry heaving. I wanted to stand over her in her worst moment and scream that she was a liar, a faker, a Shitbag, as she had done to me. But my anger gave way. I pitied her unborn child and the chaos it was entering. I hoped her impending motherhood would soften her, make her attuned to the suffering in others, but I doubted it would. My mother felt nothing except for her own woes. Climbing into the passenger seat, Sergeant Bennett shouted for me to drive before I made her miss her appointment.

Not long after, Sergeant Bennett was ordered to quarters in the barracks, then vanished from my consciousness. A quiet, almost-calmness, fell over the warehouse. The peacefulness couldn't be attributed only to Sergeant Bennett's disappearance. It was then that I became aware of the absence of someone else—Sergeant Bluff. He had been gone for days, a week. In this new calm, I had lost track of time. His slow fading away began right after the IG's visit to speak with us in the SSA.

When I asked my comrades where he was, they replied in whispered and hushed words. Officially, they said, Sergeant Bluff had hurt his Achilles, so the First Sergeant allowed him to work from home while he recovered. Unofficially, they claimed after the whole IG investigation, the First Sergeant banished him. They heard that Sergeant Bluff's actions had embarrassed not only himself, but his old buddy the First Sergeant. Although there was not enough evidence to charge him with anything, my comrades told me, the First Sergeant said he was done with him. He wanted him out of the platoon, out of the company.

I wondered how such a scenario was possible. What was a platoon sergeant without a platoon? My comrades said Sergeant Bluff lost the SSA—the platoon, the warehouse—everything. When they saw him stop by to pick up some files, they knew he was reduced to nothing more than a broke-down NCO in charge of managing and controlling inventory from his couch. Sergeant Samuels now calls the platoon to attention every morning. He now sits up front in Sergeant Bluff's old office.

What my fellow soldiers didn't say, but I heard in their laughter, was that this was Sergeant Bluff's punishment. I wanted to believe it, I wanted to think of him suffering and crying for his loss, but I couldn't. I imagined he was happy to have a vacation from the stress. But then, yesterday, while pushing a cart of supplies through the bins in the Issue Section of the warehouse, I caught my first glimpse of Sergeant Bluff in weeks.

In a chair usually reserved for customers, he slumped forward. In his lap was a manilla folder stuffed with papers. His unshaven face had broken out in large cysts. The high-and-tight buzz cut he had once worn had been replaced with a loppy, grown-out shag. His muscular frame had turned lumpy and soft, and due to his lack of PT, he had grown a slight hump on his back. Propped beside him was a set of wooden crutches. His left foot, wrapped fat in a white bandage, stretched out in front of him. With our dual Achilles injuries, we were at last matched.

I came out from behind the issue bin where I stood, daring him to look at me. I thought of how much he was like my father who lashed out when I refused to give him what he demanded. I could not show either of them enough respect, enough love, enough obedience to suit them, so they made me suffer. If I would have just given both men what they wanted, then I would not have invited this hell onto myself. I could never kneel before any man, and I swore I never would.

Sergeant Bluff stood up on one foot and put his crutches under his arms. He hobbled to the double doors and struggled with the handle. He pushed open one of the doors. A crack of sunlight poured into the dark warehouse. Without a word, he was gone into the unknown.

These days, the SSA pulses with a different energy. James, Romero, and Abela bicker like siblings. They argue over which song to play on the little black boom box, before compromising and settling into the groove of the music. Sergeant Samuels rambles through the back of the warehouse. Women soldiers on forklifts jump down and ask him to please order pink hard hats.

He laughs and says okay. Then walking over to my workstation, he compliments me on my pressed uniform, on the good job I've been doing lately. I am so squared away now, all of us in the back of the warehouse are, he says. What changed?

Nothing, everything, I think. We have always been squared away, but that never aligned with Sergeant Bluff's reality. If we stand a little taller, if we walk with a little more confidence, it is only because at last others see us for how we really are. This is how it should have always been. I can't believe that it is only now, after so many of us women and Sergeant Donahue with his rank and maleness backing up our stories that someone believed us.

I wonder what my buddies, Dale, Dix, and Low would think about this place now. I spoke out, we all did, individually at different times, but no one believed us. If they had, then maybe we would all still be here together. Low would have requested to extend his tour in Germany, instead of taking a new assignment. Dale, Dix, and I would not have chosen to end our Army careers.

What will happen to all of us now, I ask myself. I think of Dix, who left in the middle of a late winter night. He was only a PFC, fresh out of AIT, and in less than a year he was kicked out for an "indiscretion". I will never know the truth of what happened, although the guys in the barracks said he put his dick in someone he shouldn't have. They claim the company wanted the whole event swept under the rug, so the Command issued him a quick Honorable Discharge.

Dix was never a gung-ho Army guy. In Poland, he spoke of home, with his mom too busy caring for his little brother to even notice him. I can't imagine he was too happy to return. He would never admit it, though. None of us would. We all say we can't wait to be civilians again. We tell ourselves a fairytale version of home, different from the one we left. It makes me wonder if someday we will craft different versions of our Army stories, complete with happy endings.

Dale already rewrote his story before he left. When I first met him he talked about how he was going to reenlist, maybe even apply to OCS, Officer Candidate School. Then one morning early last spring, in formation Sergeant Bluff said he smelled alcohol on Dale's breath. Dale was busted down from Specialist to Private weeks before he was due to re-up. Later he told me he had no good options: He could reenlist and start over at the bottom, or for the rest of his life he would have DD-214 that said after four years, he was only a Private. Although his discharge would be Honorable, his good service would be erased.

As the weather became clearer, so too did Dale's choice. He said he was at peace with everything. He was relieved to go back to the civilian world after all this Army bullshit. But on our desk calendar, with a blood-red Sharpie, he slashed off the days remaining until he left. He never told me goodbye, he just disappeared. I try to take it as a compliment. On Low's last day, he refused to say goodbye. He didn't like a big drawn out scene at the end, he said.

From the trash bin, I rescued the calendar page with Dale's scratches. Inside the date squares, in that same red Sharpie he had scrawled, "Thirty days and a wake-up... twenty-nine days... twenty-eight..." In the right-hand margin, in all caps, he had written "FTA," echoing that same sentiment he said in Poland. Yeah, FTA, I thought, and fuck that NATO mission. As I continued to reminisce, though, my memories sweetened. We had some good times together, I thought.

Then my memories turn to Low, and our times together picking up trash, policing up brass on the range, being sent to the field. With him, those duties were never a punishment. Maybe because his Army story isn't ending, his is the only one not tinged with sadness.

In a letter with a Texas postmark, he wrote how much he liked his new duty station. He was in a great unit, with great comrades, and already his Command was putting him up for promotion to sergeant. He asked how I was doing, how was Dale and Dix. But I never wrote him back. I can't lie, but I can't tell him the truth.

When I call home, I have no problem not telling Mom the truth. I don't want her to say she told me so, that she knew I would fail. So, I tell her I won. I'm thrilled. I'm coming home, alive. She tells me I had better be sure that is what I want. I wonder if she is disappointed with my coming home. Maybe she is disappointed I am coming home alive. Now she cannot tell the story of her brave, heroic daughter she sacrificed for the good of the nation.

"When you come home, it's best if you never talk about the Army," she says, her words piercing me from thousands of miles away. "There is no way to explain to people what happened. Nothing happened, but you're broken. Just like I said it would, the Army broke you."

I hang up and throw the phone onto the bed. Across the room, in my dresser mirror, I check out my reflection. Mom is still the same person she always was, but I feel different. I look different. My short red hair has grown long enough to gather into a small pony tail. My face is pale from not enough sleep and exercise, and puffy from too many prescriptions, like antibiotics, muscle relaxers, and ibuprofen. My BDUs hug my hips and chest, betraying that I am a woman with breasts and hips. I see someone who is not broken, but who has survived. I don't understand how Mom sees something, someone so different than I do.

The Army, the world, the whole universe, everything looks different to me now. I no longer believe fairy tales are true, but I believe in a deeper truth. Underneath the story of my time in the Army is something else. The world is not black and white, it isn't even gray. It is full of color beyond the wavelengths visible to our eyes. On a recent road march, when the Earth was beginning to thaw in early spring, I glimpsed an entire other spectrum I had never seen before.

Marching up a winding, forested path beside my comrades, dressed in full battle rattle, I carried my M-16 in my hands and a full rucksack on my back. I struggled to keep up on the march as my back spasmed and my left ankle ached. I could hardly breathe after another bout of bronchitis. As the sun rose over the looming trees, a sadness draped over me. It was time to admit I could no longer do this. I knew this would be the last time I ever marched with a ruck on my back, wore a Kevlar on my head, or carried my M-16. My time in the Army was ending.

After marching for hours through the cool Bavarian forest, our figures shielded from sunlight by the dense canopy of evergreens, we shivered and sweated. My body folded under my burden. I bowed my head, uncertain if I could push my broken body any further. Falling out of this march was not an option. I would not leave my fellow soldiers with the last memory of me saying I couldn't make it. I had to find the strength to keep pushing.

Returning to formation, I marched ahead. I stared into the distance and through the trees my eyes latched on to something. It reflected the sunlight and sparkled. We moved closer, and after several meters, I at last made out what it was, or what I thought it was. From deep in the forest rose a glistening, golden palace. It didn't make sense. I had never heard about a castle all the way out in the middle of the woods. Maybe it was a rare cold weather mirage in the trees.

I waited for my fellow soldiers to say something, to acknowledge they saw what I did. No one said a word. We continued to march in the direction of the structure. Confused, still not trusting my eyes, I asked a soldier beside me, "Is that... Is that a castle? Are we marching to a castle?"

He chuckled, "It would appear so."

My feet fell into the rhythm of the march. We continued up the muddy forest trail until at last I was staring up at a real-life royal palace. We passed through a set of doors into a courtyard. Wearing our Kevlar helmets and carrying our rucksacks and M-16s, we marched past trimmed boxwoods, dormant roses, marble statues, and a stone fountain. We walked through an arching corridor, past clock towers reaching toward the sky. Overhead domes loomed from each corner of the roof. Through some heavy ornate double doors, sunlight streamed, and on the other side, was my old life, my new life. Pausing before the doorway, I surveyed the beauty of the architecture while my comrades marched on.

"C'mon, Burton," a soldier shouted. "We're leaving."

"Go on without me," I yelled back.

As I turned to look back at the courtyard, my feet were less anchored to the ground, my body less bound to this world. I shut my eyes and saw the soldiers who had come before me, stopping as I did to gaze upon this very castle. Little more than young country kids plucked from the middle of America, they found themselves marching with the Army across Europe. They were not who they used to be anymore, nor were they the hardened fighting machines they so often portrayed. Until then all they had seen was the suffering and ugliness of battle. But here, unexpectedly, they found themselves in the middle of something more beautiful than they could imagined. This was a place that existed only in fairy tales, yet here it was in real life, in a grandeur of gold walls and green gardens. In the few moments they paused to take it all in, they realized how they had changed because of all they experienced. Nothing in their lives back home came close to the highs, the lows, the drudgery, and excitement here. And no one back home, no matter how they framed the story, would ever fully comprehend.

As I floated down, I looked out the doorway. The formation of soldiers marched away, growing smaller until they resembled the green plastic toy soldiers from my girlhood. I grappled to make peace with the past, with a new future that had come too soon. In my new old world I would be an American, a college student, maybe even a veteran. I would not be a Shitbag nor would I be a soldier. I would never be a soldier again.

Outside the doors of the palace, I knelt and picked a tender violet flower, one unlike I had ever seen growing in Kentucky. I put it to my nose. Its delicate petals felt like velvet, its stem and leaves were coated in mud. It smelled purple and Army Green, like wool socks and baby powder, like lavender and bullshit.

I tucked the flower under the elastic band circling my Kevlar. I put my face toward the sun high in the noonday sky. I let the formation drift off into the horizon without me.

Acknowledgments

Acknowledgements

Without comrades, friends, and battle buddies, I would have never written this book.

I am so thankful to Tony Acree of Hydra for this opportunity to tell my story.

A million thank yous to my husband, Michael Schliesman, who saved my sanity by serving as my editor, sounding board, and emotional support over the years as I took writing classes, attended therapy, did yoga, and cried. To the counselors and medical staff at the Department of Veterans Affairs, thank you feels inadequate. Thanks to Nate's Coffee for powering me up to write. Hugs and kisses to my pug Lucy whose need to play and potty got me out of the house a few times. And R.I.P., Pugsie, who sat next to me during the first, first drafts.

I appreciate the writers and instructors at the Carnegie Center for Literacy and Learning for helping me not only to become a better writer, but for showing me how telling a painful story can bring meaning to life.

To Erv Klein, Lindsay Gargotto, Angie Gray, Phyllis Abbott, Adrielle Stapleton, Linda Freudenberger, Rosemary James, James Campbell, Bill Carmen, Judy Matthews, Nancy McKenney, Leatha Kendrick, Katerina Stoykova, Laverne Zabielski, Ron Whitehead, Michael Johnathon, Lee Pennington, Laura Womack, Carla Cilvik, Callie Rowland, and everyone else who believed not only in this project, but in me, even when I didn't—thank you for everything.

Vielen Dank, thank you, to the magazine *Alice Says Go Fuck Yourself* for publishing my chapter "Fieldstripped" in their second issue, *The Dying Light*. Thank you to Crystal Wilkinson for airing a recording of an excerpt of "Fieldstripped" on her podcast *Words for the People*.

I cannot ever thank my cousin and second grade teacher, Thelma Buell, enough. She instilled in me a love of expressing myself though words. When I swore I had written everything I ever could, she said she bet if I sat down and thought hard, I still had a few more stories to write.

About the Author

Lubrina Burton is a veteran of the United States Army. Her experience as a young enlisted soldier in a pre-9/11 military inspires much of her work. After the Army, she graduated from Eastern Kentucky University in Richmond, Kentucky, and later, the Carnegie Center's Author Academy in Lexington. Her short pieces are featured in That Southern Thing, Trouble, Curious Stuff, Twists and Turns, From Pen to Page II, and Alice Says Go Fuck Yourself. This is her first book.